The Well Being
Cookbook

Recipes, nutritional advice, breathing and relaxation techniques.

Written by Jeanne Rankin
with Niamh McDaid and Deirdre Conlon
on behalf of Cancer Focus Northern Ireland.

British Library Cataloguing in Publication Data.
A catalogue record of this book is available from the British Library.

ISBN: 978-0-9520223-1-2

Copyright Cancer Focus Northern Ireland 2014

This edition was published in 2014

Published by Cancer Focus Northern Ireland,
40-44 Eglantine Avenue, Belfast BT9 6DX

Printed in Northern Ireland

There are many differing ideas, theories and sometimes sensational media stories about diet and cancer, both during and after diagnosis. If you are living with cancer, the chances are you have already become more aware of what you eat and drink. This can be a helpful process in that you can learn about how diet can aid your recovery and possibly help you to stay well in the future. Taking an interest in your daily food may help you feel empowered at a time when so much of your 'being' can feel out of your own hands.

As a trained chef, I know the value
of good food, prepared simply.
In this book we hope to offer you
recipe ideas that will help you in a
practical way to manage to eat well
and keep up your energy levels.
Even the information, hints and tips
may inspire you to take a little time in
the kitchen to help care for yourself.
Hopefully we have chosen simple
recipes that are easy to make and
will not seem too much of an effort
at times when your energy is low.
And the togetherness that can be
felt when good food is shared and
enjoyed with family or friends can
offer unique inner healing through
the act of 'breaking bread'.

Most of us will get what we need from
a healthy and balanced diet. If you
have other pre-existing health issues
or problems with recovery during and
after your cancer treatment, you may
find it helpful to talk to your specialist
team, especially the dietician at your
cancer centre.

Jeanne

Jeanne Rankin

Keeping healthy after a cancer diagnosis

It's all well and good to say follow a healthy balanced diet; however when you're going through any type of cancer treatment eating a nutritious balanced diet can be hard to do. Especially if you're dealing with side effects from treatment or you just don't feel well in general.

NUTRITION

Healthy eating, during and after cancer will help you feel better, stay stronger and keep your energy levels high. It will also help you fight infection, tolerate treatment side-effects better and recover faster.

During your cancer treatment, you may need to change your diet to suit your own needs and even eat foods that are usually not recommended. For example, you may need to eat high fat or high calorie foods to keep or regain your weight. For example, you could:

- add cream or cheese to sauces and soups to add flavour

- add ice cream to milkshakes and yoghurt to smoothies

EAT A ·bit of· every-thing & never DIET!

SAUCE

Everything in Moderation!

YOUR DAILY EATWELL PLATE

Eat a variety of different foods every day which will give you essential nutrients. Follow the Eatwell plate to ensure you get the balance right. Eat fruit and vegetables to provide essential vitamins and minerals; protein for growth and repair; carbohydrates for energy and dairy products for calcium and bone strength.

Eat small frequent meals/ snacks throughout the day

When it comes to a healthy diet, balance is the key to getting it right. This means eating a wide variety of foods in the right proportions, and consuming the right amount of food and drink to achieve and maintain a healthy body weight.

Eat fruit and vegetables to provide essential vitamins and minerals;

carbs = energy

choose wholegrain

PLENTY OF BREAD, RICE, POTATOES, PASTA

LOTS OF FRUIT & VEGETABLES

SOME PROTEIN

Protein for growth and repair.

JUST A LITTLE FATS & SUGARS

SOME MILK & DAIRY

Dairy for calcium and bone strength

FOOD LABELLING
making sense of it all

Food labels are a source of useful information about a food. It shows the nutritional content of a food and will inform you if it has high, medium or low amounts of fat, saturated fat, salt and sugars per 100 g. Traffic light colours can help you make the healthy choice quickly and easily.

TRAFFIC LIGHT CODE:

Green – food is LOW in a particular nutrient. Green is the healthiest option so the more green the better.

Amber – food has MEDIUM amounts. If a food has mostly amber that means you can eat the food most of the time.

Red – food is HIGH in that nutrient. We should try and cut down on these products and eat them less often.

Not all food products have the traffic light system on the packaging but use this table to determine how healthy a product is for you. You could copy this table and keep it in your purse or wallet for reference when you are out shopping.

Nutrition Fac

Serving Size Entire Recipe 187g

Amount Per Serving

Calories   Calories fro

Per 100 g measure	Low (Healthier choice)	Medium	High (only occasionally)
Sugars	<5 g	5.1 g – 15 g	>15 g
Fat	<3 g	3.1 g – 20 g	>20 g
Saturates	<1.5 g	1.6 g – 5 g	>5 g
Salt	<0.3 g	0.31 g – 1.5 g	>1.5 g

% Daily

Trans Fat

lesterol 0mg

Helpful tips

Snacks to boost your calorie intake:

Buttered popcorn

Chocolate milk or milk shakes

Cereal

Cream soups

Dried fruits (raisins, prunes, apricots)

Ice creams, frozen yogurts

Peanut butter

Fruits (fresh or canned)

Hard boiled eggs

Nuts

Crackers

If you have a Dry Mouth...

- Drink 8 glasses of water a day. Carry a bottle of water throughout the day.

- Fruit such as pineapple can be very refreshing to eat or drink and will help keep your taste buds working.

- Moisten foods with gravy, soup, sauces, cream or yoghurts.

- Suck on sugar free sweets and mints, or chew gum to stimulate saliva.

- Eat soft, moist foods that are cool or at room temperature. Try blending fruits and vegetables, soft-cooked chicken and fish, well-thinned cereals (e.g. Weetabix), into a puree for easier swallowing.

- Avoid foods that stick to the roof of the mouth like peanut butter or soft bread.

ALCOHOL

If you consume alcohol at all, limit alcohol to 1 drink a day for women and 2 drinks a day for men.

1 small glass of wine
= 1 drink,
1 pint beer/cider
= 2 drinks,
1 measure of gin/vodka/run
= 1 drink

Be careful with!

- Avoid processed foods, they can be high in fat, salt and sugar.

- Limit your red meat consumption. Choose chicken, turkey and fish as a source of protein.

- Limit dairy products to 2—4 portions a week, unless you are needing the calories. 1 portion is equal to a match box size of cheese or a 200 ml glass of milk.

Things to remember

- Eat small frequent meals/snacks throughout the day

- Eat your favourite foods at any time of the day. E.g. eat your breakfast food at dinnertime if that's what you prefer.

- Do a bit of physical activity e.g. go for a walk, swim or do some gardening before meals to increase your appetite.

- Drink plenty of fluids throughout the day. Carry a bottle of water with you everywhere.

- If you eat well during cancer treatment, you are better able to cope with the side effects. This will help you get through treatment and afterwards will give you energy and strength as you recover.

- Try changing the time, place and surroundings of your meals to increase appetite. Watching your favourite TV programme or listening to your favourite music may also increase appetite.

- Eat little and often during the day. Stock up on your favourite foods as you are more likely to enjoy eating them.

- Choose foods that look and smell good to you. Try flavouring meat, chicken and fish by marinating it in sweet fruit sauces, or sweet and sour sauce. Add herbs and spices to meals to increase the flavour.

Oven temperature conversion table

Description	Deg. C	Deg. C (fan)	Gas Mark
Cool	110	90	¼
	120	100	½
Low	140	120	1
	150	130	2
Moderate	160	140	3
	180	160	4
Moderately hot	190	170	5
	200	180	6
Hot	220	200	7
	230	210	8
Very hot	240	220	9

FOOD SAFETY AND YOUR IMMUNE SYSTEM

Some cancer treatments can put stress on your immune system so take extra care with the preparation, cooking and storage of food.

- Always wash your hands before beginning to prepare or eat any food.

- During preparation of food, be sure to wash your hands after coughing or sneezing, blowing your nose, going to the toilet or handling animals.

- Wash fruit and vegetables thoroughly. Scrub the outside even if you do not eat it.

- Keep meat and fish separate from other foods (cooked or raw). Wash hands and utensils after working with them before preparing anything else.

- Be careful when reheating food. It must be heated through to 73°C. Don't reheat foods twice and avoid reheating rice and take-away meals.

- Check storage conditions recommended on food labels and the storage time once the product has been opened

- Store raw meat and fish at the bottom of the fridge.

- Don't keep foods past their use-by date. This is an indicator that they are past the point of being safe to eat. Check your fridge and cupboards for any mouldy foods and discard them.

- Don't add raw chicken to cooked food – cook the chicken first or separately.

THE STORE CUPBOARD
Seasonal eating

_____

Eating what is in season is good for the environment, good for our farmers and good for you. Although some vegetables and fruits are available all year long, you get to experience a wider variety of fresh produce as they go in and out of season.

More reasons to eat local seasonal food:

- It tastes better.

- It may contain nutrients that suit your body's needs better for that time of year.

- Your food will not have travelled for as long and will be fresher with more nutrients and vitamins retained.

- There will be less preservatives needed to keep your food fresh.

- Food allergies and intolerances might lessen because you don't eat the same foods day after day.

- Locally produced food will be cheaper to buy.

A well-stocked food cupboard in the kitchen will help make shopping for and planning meals a much easier task. Most of the following dried and tinned foods have a reasonable shelf life and are both inexpensive and easily available in shops and supermarkets.

The basics

- **Flour** - plain, self-raising, wholemeal and cornflour
- **Sugars** - granulated, caster, icing and Demerara
- **Dried pasta and Asian style noodles**
- **Rice** - basmati, wholegrain or long grain
- **Grains** - bulgur, cous cous, quinoa
- **Dried & tinned beans & pulses** - lentils, kidney beans, butterbeans, chickpeas
- **Dried fruits** - dates, apricots, sultanas, raisins
- **Nuts & seeds** - almonds, sunflower, pumpkin, hazelnuts

Useful

- **Tinned tomatoes & tomato puree**
- **Tinned fish** e.g. sardines, tuna, salmon
- **Tinned fruits** (in their own juice)
- **Low salt stock cubes** & dried soup mix
- **Dried herbs**, spices, salt & pepper
- **Vinegar** - cider, rice wine & balsamic
- **Oils** such as sunflower, olive, rape, sesame and nut oils
- **Garlic, chilli and spice pastes** such as pesto, low fat soy sauce

FATIGUE
FIGHTING

FATIGUE FIGHTING

Spicy Avocado Guacamole

Super Green Juice with Chia Seeds

Thai Green Curry Turkey Breast Steaks

Healthy Vegetable Soup with Rice and Lentils

Quinoa Salad with Avocado and Tomato

Roast Beetroots, Walnuts and Spinach Salad

Peppered Tuna Steak with Salsa and Avocado

Traditional Oat Porridge with Maple Syrup and Berries

Sweet Quinoa Porridge

If you are feeling tired and just want to get on with your daily routine, go for protein. These recipes are high in protein which is important for growth, repair and to keep your immune systems healthy.

After surgery, chemotherapy or radiation therapy your body needs extra protein to heal tissues and to help fight infection.

SPICY AVOCADO GUACAMOLE

Serves 2-3

---

2 small to medium ripe avocados

Juice of 1 lime

1 garlic clove, finely chopped

2 Tbsp fresh coriander, chopped

1 fresh red or green chilli,
seeded and finely chopped

Salt and freshly ground white pepper

In a small glass bowl, mash the avocado flesh until it is a rough, slightly lumpy puree. (A potato masher does the job well...) Stir in the lime juice immediately as this preserves the colour. Stir in the garlic and coriander. Add the chilli. Try adding half the quantity first, and taste and adjust as necessary. Give the avocado a few minutes to absorb the flavour before adding more. Add the salt and pepper to taste.

Use immediately, or cover with cling film and place in the fridge for up to two days.

Serve with corn tortilla chips, pitta bread, or freshly chopped carrot and celery sticks.

Diced fresh tomato adds colour and flavour.

Avocado provides an excellent source of nutritious protein. It also contains an abundance of vitamins and minerals and its fats are the healthy mono saturated type. It is also high in lecithin, which is a brain food.

SUPER GREEN JUICE WITH CHIA SEEDS

Makes 2 glasses (approx 500 ml)

---

2 apples, quartered (Pink Lady)

1 lime, skin removed (or 1 lemon)

2 stalks celery

½ cucumber, halved

1 loosely filled cup kale leaves, roughly chopped

50 g (approx 3 Tbsp) curly parsley,
big stems removed

2 cm piece ginger (optional)

½-1 Tbsp chia seeds, ready milled

Juice everything except the chia seeds.
Pour into 2 glasses and stir in the chia seeds.
If you prefer it sweeter, add another apple.

Chia is the richest plant based food source of Omega 3, fibre and protein. They are easier to digest milled.

Parsley can relieve water retention and can strengthen digestion when taken in juiced form.

THAI GREEN CURRY TURKEY BREAST STEAKS

Serves 2

2-4 turkey breasts
(approx 180-240 g / 6-8 oz per person)

2 Tbsp olive oil

1 onion, chopped

3 garlic cloves, pressed

1 green chilli, seeded and sliced

4 cm piece ginger, chopped

1 stalk lemon grass, finely sliced

1 tsp white pepper

1 ½ tsp ground coriander

1 tsp ground cumin

1 tsp turmeric

1 Tbsp thai fish sauce

1 tin coconut milk

Handful Thai basil, or basil leaves, chopped

Heat the oil in a heavy fry pan over medium heat. Season the turkey breast steaks with salt and sauté them off, approx 3-4 minutes each side. Remove them from the pan, and tip in the onion, garlic, chilli, ginger, and lemon grass. Sauté off for approx 3 – 4 minutes. Add the spices, and cook for a further minute. Add the fish sauce and the coconut milk and turn the heat to low.

The turkey meat can be sliced, or added back to the sauce as whole steaks. Simmer over low heat for 10 minutes to allow flavours to blend. Lastly, toss in the basil.

Serve with rice or Asian style noodles.

Like chicken, turkey is highly nutritious; low in fat; and an excellent source of protein, iron and zinc. Do not be put off by the length of the list of spices. Simply measure them out into a bowl while the turkey is cooking and they will be ready to toss into the sauce.

HEALTHY VEGETABLE SOUP WITH RICE AND LENTILS

Serves 4

---

1 Tbsp olive oil

1 medium leek, finely sliced

2 cloves of garlic, chopped
(or 2 tsp of Lazy garlic)

2 medium carrots, grated

1 stick celery, peeled and finely chopped

60 g (approx 4 Tbsp) brown rice

60 g (approx 4 Tbsp) green or brown lentils

2 litres water

2 vegetable stock cubes

2 sprigs fresh thyme or ½ tsp dried

240 g (approx 1 cup) fresh or frozen edamame beans (or peas)

4-6 Tbsp fresh parsley, chopped

Heat oil in a large pot over medium heat and add leeks, garlic, carrots, and celery. Sauté until tender, about 10-15 minutes. Add liquid, stock cubes, rice, lentils and thyme.

Bring to boil and then simmer for about 30 minutes, until rice and lentils are tender.

Add edamame beans (or peas) if using, and heat until they are hot also.

Add chopped parsley.

This soup is full of nutrition from the fresh vegetables and complementary protein from the grain and pulses. Parsley is aromatic and tasty so use generously.

Another grain such as barley could replace the rice. Chickpeas or other pulse could replace the lentils. Adjust cooking time accordingly.

Make double the recipe and store in fridge or freezer.

QUINOA SALAD WITH AVOCADO AND TOMATO

Serves 3-4

---

2 Tbsp olive oil

1 medium white onion finely chopped

1 packet quinoa (300 g)

450 ml boiling water

½ tsp salt

1-3 green chillies, seeded and finely chopped (depends on taste)

Juice of 1-2 limes

1 avocado, finely chopped and tossed in lime juice

½ punnet cherry tomatoes, halved or quartered

Extra virgin olive oil

1 small bunch fresh coriander leaf, chopped

2-3 Tbsp freshly chopped parsley or mint

Ground black pepper

Heat the olive oil in a medium pan. Sauté off the onion over medium heat until translucent. Pour the quinoa grain into the pan, and add boiling water and salt. Cover with lid and place over low heat for approx 5 minutes. Remove from heat and leave to steam for a further 5-10 minutes. Stir in the green chillies, and leave to cool.

When just warm, or at room temperature, stir in the avocado and lime juice, tomatoes and chopped coriander. Taste for seasoning, add a bit more salt and / or lime juice if desired. Garnish with the extra virgin olive oil, chopped parsley or mint and ground black pepper.

This will keep in fridge in covered container overnight. Or make it to the cooled stage, and add the salad ingredients to just the amount being eaten, and store the rest of the cooked quinoa in the fridge for up to 3 days.

Quinoa is so light and easy to digest and yet is full of digestible proteins. It is a powerhouse food. It can be served warm with a store bought pasta or chili sauce ladled over for a quick and easy meal.

ROAST BEETROOT, WALNUTS AND SPINACH SALAD

Serves 2

225 g / 1 lb fresh beetroot

45 g walnuts, toasted and roughly chopped

½ bag of washed spinach, approx 250 g

2 Tbsp feta cheese, crumbled – optional

Vinaigrette:

75 ml / ¼ cup olive oil

2 Tbsp Balsamic vinegar

2 tsp honey

Salt and freshly ground pepper

Preheat oven to 160°C.

Wash and trim each bulb of beetroot. Wrap each in some aluminum foil and place in a moderate oven for approx. 1 hour (if the beetroot are large, cut into halves or quarters). When pierced easily with a fork, they are cooked. Remove from oven and allow cooling. Peel and chop.

Place all the ingredients in a large bowl. Combine the vinaigrette dressing and mix well. Pour over the salad and toss.

Serve at once.

Substitute a shop bought vinaigrette or even store bought cooked beetroot if you are low on energy or short on time. Goat's cheese may be used instead of feta.

Thinly sliced fennel adds a lovely crunch to this salad and fennel is a digestive aid.

Spinach is nourishing, exceptionally rich in iron and folic acid and is best eaten raw. It is thought to be good for cancer protection as it is full of the whole spectrum of carotenoids (not just beta-carotene).

PEPPERED TUNA STEAK WITH SALSA AND AVOCADO

Serves 2

---

300 g / ¾ lb very fresh tuna, cut into 2 steaks

Salt

30 g (2 level Tbsp) cracked black peppercorns

1-2 Tbsp light olive oil

Jar of good quality salsa (as hot as you like)

1 small, ripe avocado

Juice of lime

Salt and pepper

To prepare the tuna, first trim the tuna steaks of any dark flesh or skin. Season the steaks lightly with salt and then coat each steak evenly with the cracked pepper, pressing it firmly into the tuna steaks with your hand. Coat lightly in the oil and refrigerate until ready to cook.

To cook the tuna, heat a large heavy frying pan over a high heat. Sear the tuna steaks for approximately 1 minute on each side depending on thickness of the steak, and then remove to warm serving plates.

Chop the avocado and toss liberally in the lime juice. Place a generous spoonful of the salsa on top of the tuna steak, and sprinkle the avocado over the top.

This could be served with rice or potato or a green salad.

Tuna is known to contain high levels of the fatty acids belonging to the Omega 3 family-essential to healthy cell function.

TRADITIONAL OAT PORRIDGE WITH MAPLE SYRUP AND BERRIES

Serves 2

550 ml water

100 g oatmeal

Dash salt

Almond or soy milk

Maple syrup

Fresh or frozen berries

Honey

Optional sliced nuts, ground hemp or flax

Place the water on to boil in a heavy bottomed saucepan. Stir in the oats and reduce heat immediately to a very low heat. Stir occasionally to prevent sticking and cook for 5 to 10 minutes. The longer it cooks, the thicker the consistency will be. Add the salt at the end.

To serve, place the porridge in the bowls, drizzle with almond or soy milk, maple syrup and top with a spoonful or two of berries. Some toasted sliced almonds or sliced hazelnuts add some crunch.

Ground hemp or flax can be sprinkled over instead of sliced nuts.

Oats are outstanding in their nutritional value - high in protein, rich in Vitamin E, some of the B vitamins and minerals, particularly zinc, manganese and silica.

They are said to be helpful in fatigue and strengthening the heart.

SWEET QUINOA PORRIDGE

Serves 2

125 g quinoa

1 small apple, grated

1 tsp cinnamon

Dash salt

200 ml boiling water

100 ml unsweetened rice or almond milk

Fresh or frozen blueberries

3 Tbsp toasted flaked almonds

Brown sugar to sprinkle
(or drizzle with honey)

Place the quinoa, grated apple, cinnamon and salt in a small saucepan and pour the boiling water over. Bring back to the boil over high heat, and soon as it is bubbling reduce the heat to simmer, and cook covered for 10-15 minutes, until the water is all absorbed. Stir in the milk and let steam, covered for a further 5 minutes.

Place the quinoa in bowls and top with fresh blueberries, toasted almond flakes, and a generous sprinkling of brown sugar and serve at once (if using frozen blueberries, add them with the milk and allow the steaming porridge to thaw them). If desired a further drizzle of almond milk can be added with the garnishes.

The protein content of quinoa is the highest of any grain, both in quantity and quality. It is also the most easy to digest. It is a very good source of iron, vitamin B, vitamin E and phosphorus, and has more calcium than milk.

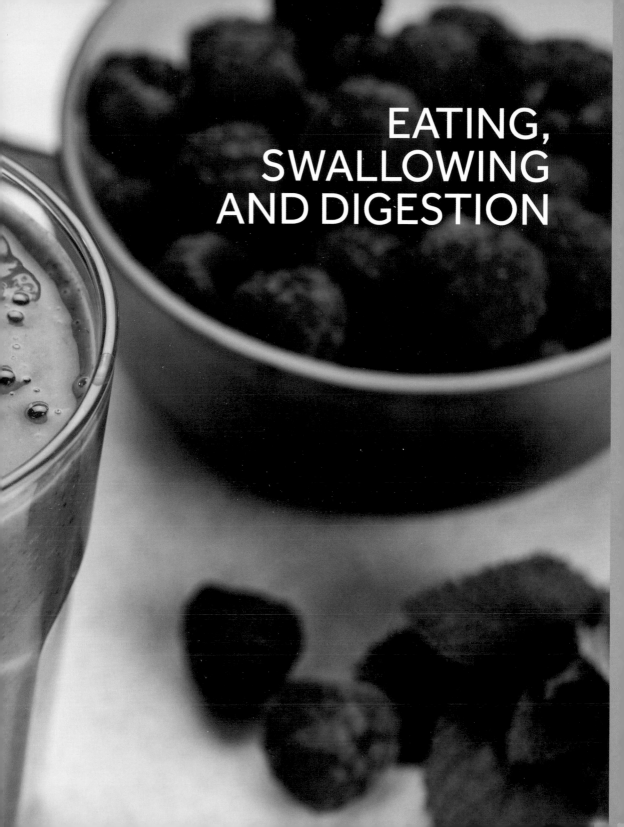

EATING, SWALLOWING AND DIGESTION

EATING, SWALLOWING AND DIGESTION LIST

Banana Raspberry Smoothie

Pineapple Coconut Smoothie

Herb and Lemon Chicken Breasts

Simple Baked Salmon with a Honey Mustard Glaze

Warm Spicy Sweet Potato Salad

Pureed Carrot, Ginger and Lentil Soup

Potato and Fennel Champ

Ginger Lemongrass Tea

Warm Sweet Spiced Almond Milk

It can be difficult to eat anything during or after treatment. These recipes are all easy to swallow, tasty and soothing. Using fragrant herbs and pungent spices will help to make food more appealing if you have lost your sense of taste as they will brighten the aroma of foods. Remember to take small bites, and perhaps moisten or soak foods with soup or gravy. The smoothies can be taken through a straw.

BANANA AND RASPBERRY SMOOTHIE

Serves 2

---

1 banana, sliced

200 g frozen raspberries (approx 1 ½ cups)

1 Tbsp honey

300 g low fat natural yogurt
(or 300 ml almond/coconut/rice milk)

1 Tbsp vanilla whey protein powder (optional)

1-2 tsp flax seed oil (optional)

Place all the ingredients in a blender and blend until smooth. Serve at once.

Flax seeds are full of Omega 3, vitamins and minerals, and a great low GI food. In oil form it is the richest source of the Omega-3 fatty acid, vitally important for strengthening immunity.

Tip: Peel and slice over ripe bananas and keep in self sealing sandwich bag in freezer. Substitute for the fresh banana.

PINEAPPLE COCONUT SMOOTHIE

Serves 2

250 g frozen pineapple chunks
(approx 2 cups)

200 ml coconut milk

Juice of 1 orange
(or 100 ml orange juice)

Juice of 1 lime

Blend together until smooth. This smoothie has a silky texture from the coconut milk.

Use a coconut milk that doesn't have additives and stabilisers. It is rich in zinc and potassium. You can get a reduced fat version. Coconut is considered a tonic and is used for weakness conditions.

HERB AND LEMON CHICKEN BREASTS

Serves 2

---

2 x 150 g (5 oz) skinless chicken breasts

1 Tbsp olive oil

For the herb marinade:

1 tsp dried thyme

1 tsp dried rosemary

1 tsp dried parsley

1 tsp freshly ground black pepper

1 tsp lemon zest

1 Tbsp lemon juice

1 tsp sugar

4 Tbsp olive oil

Make the marinade by whisking together all the ingredients in a medium sized bowl. Toss the chicken in the marinade and leave to marinate for at least 60 minutes to overnight. To cook the chicken, remove it from the marinade, and season with salt.

Heat the second olive oil in a heavy bottomed fry pan; it is just enough to coat the bottom of the pan. Over medium heat, place the breasts in and cook for 10-12 minutes on each side, depending on the thickness of the breasts.

Reduce the heat a little if the herb mixture is catching. If this is the case, lengthen the cooking time accordingly.

Serve with a green salad and potatoes of your choice.

There are great Italian or Greek herb mixes available in most supermarkets that could be substituted for this herb mix with the same delicious results.

Cook the breasts plain and drizzle with a mint pesto for a flavoursome dish.

SIMPLE BAKED SALMON WITH A HONEY MUSTARD GLAZE

Serves 2

---

1 Tbsp honey

1 Tbsp smooth Dijon mustard

1 Tbsp light soy sauce

2 salmon fillets, skinned, approx 180 g each

Preheat oven to 140°C.

Lightly oil a ceramic baking dish. Place the salmon in skinned, side down.

Whisk together all the ingredients and spread glaze evenly over each fillet.

Bake until cooked through, about 5-10 minutes depending on thickness of fillets.

Serve at once.

A meat substitute such as Quorn could also replace the fish. Cook to the length of time manufacturer suggests.

This glaze would suit chicken breasts also.

Holding the knife horizontally, slice each chicken breast in half and open like a book to create a thinner piece, and cook under the grill rather than a slow oven. Place the chicken breasts on a lightly oiled oven tray, and slide the pan under a hot grill, approx 10 cm (4 inches) away from the heat. After 2-3 minutes, turn each breast and spread the glaze evenly over the meat. Continue to cook out under the heat for a further 3-4 minutes, until the chicken is just cooked.
It will be tender if it is not over cooked.

Salmon done this way is incredibly moist and tender, and melts in the mouth.
Salmon is a valuable source of the beneficial Omega-3, fatty acids, EPA and DHA.

WARM SPICY SWEET POTATO SALAD

Serves 2-4

---

2 medium sweet potatoes, peeled and roughly diced

1 medium red onion, roughly chopped

1 Tbsp plus 60 ml extra virgin olive oil

1 small bunch fresh coriander, roughly chopped

1 x 400 g tin butter beans, drained and rinsed

1 large yellow pepper, seeded and diced

1 clove garlic, finely chopped

1-2 red chillies, seeded and chopped (or chilli powder to taste)

Juice of 1 lime

½ tsp sea salt

Freshly ground black pepper

Preheat oven to 220°C.

Place sweet potatoes and onion on a baking tray and drizzle with 1 Tbsp oil, just to coat vegetables lightly. Roast for approx 20 minutes, until the sweet potatoes are tender. While they are roasting, toss together the fresh coriander, the beans, and the yellow pepper in a bowl.

To make the dressing, place the garlic, chilli, lime, salt and pepper in the food processor or blender. On pulse, add 60 ml oil and blend well.

Toss the warm vegetables with the bean mixture and pour the dressing over it all. Mix well and serve warm.

When storing sweet potatoes, keep in a cool dry place. Refrigeration can cause moulding and discolouration to occur.

The chilli could be omitted for those with digestive problems, and replaced with fresh mint. Fresh mint can relieve flatulence and indigestion. Peppermint oil is used to relieve the symptoms of IBS.

PUREED CARROT, GINGER AND ORANGE LENTIL SOUP

Serves 4-6

2 onions, chopped

½ stalk celery, chopped

3 Tbsp finely chopped fresh ginger

6 -7 carrots, grated

2 litres water

2 vegetable stock cubes
(or vegetable stock powder)

250 g orange lentils

Salt to taste

In a large saucepan, sauté off the onion, celery and fresh ginger for about 5 minutes over medium heat. Dissolve the stock cube in boiling water. Add to pan along with carrots, and lentils. Cook out over low heat for half hour. Blend. Taste and add salt to taste.

Carrots are valuable for cancer protection, beneficial for the skin and the mucous membranes. They are full of Vitamin A, B1 and B2, C and E. Cooked carrots can benefit people with weak digestion. Fresh ginger is a stimulant that strengthens digestion and discharges mucous.

POTATO AND FENNEL CHAMP

Serves 2-3

200 g floury potatoes, peeled and chopped

300 g fennel bulb, trimmed and roughly chopped

1 tsp fennel seeds, crushed

150 ml single cream

2 Tbsp butter

Salt and pepper to taste

Cook the potatoes in one pan, in boiling salted water, until tender. Drain, and leave to steam, off the heat, in pan with lid on. These can be mashed while the fennel is cooking.

Meanwhile, at the same time, melt the butter in another pan, and add the fennel and fennel seeds. Add 75 ml of water and a dash of salt. Cover and cook over medium heat for about 10-15 minutes, until the fennel pieces are soft and tender. Add the cream, bring it to the boil and then simmer for a few minutes, until the cream has thickened slightly. Puree in a food processor and return to a clean pan.

Stir in the mashed potatoes and season with salt and pepper. Serve at once.

The fennel 'cuts' the potato's starch, making this an 'easier to swallow' champ. Fennel relieves flatulence and aids digestion.

GINGER LEMONGRASS TEA

Serves 2-3

---

2 ginger tea bags

1 Tbsp sliced fresh ginger

½ stalk lemon grass,
lightly crushed

½ stick cinnamon

2 cardamom pods (optional)

750 ml boiling water

Place the boiling water in a medium
pan and add the tea bags and
spices. Simmer for 5-10 minutes,
depending on desired strength.
Strain into teacups to serve.

*This tea is wonderfully aromatic and
soothing. Lemongrass is a fragrant
tropical grass that is readily available
in supermarkets nowadays.
It has antiseptic and antibacterial
qualities.*

WARM SWEET SPICED ALMOND MILK

Serves 2

---

500 ml almond milk

1-2 cinnamon sticks

2 Tbsp ginger, roughly sliced

1 tsp ground anise (optional)

2 Tbsp honey

In a saucepan over medium heat combine
the almond milk, cinnamon, ginger and anise.
Gently heat. As soon as it is warmed through,
remove from heat. Add honey to taste, strain,
and serve. This is a lovely warm protein drink
for winter.

*Almond milk is a wonderful way to get your
proteins and Omega 3 oils. Almonds are highly
valued in traditional Indian medicine (Ayurveda).
It can alleviate coughs reduce phlegm, and
lubricate the intestines.*

*Anise helps digestion, relieves flatulence,
and improves appetite.*

This is a soothing drink just before bed.

SIMPLE
COMFORT
FOODS

SIMPLE COMFORT FOODS

Chai

Lassi Yogurt Drink

Smokey Tomato and Bacon Soup

Salmon and Leek Tart

Vegetable Frittata

Basil Pesto Macaroni and Cheese

Chicken Barley Soup

Risotto with Asparagus, Peas and Edemame

Scrambled Eggs on a Toasted Bagel and a Herbed Cream Cheese

Wholegrain Blueberry Pancakes

Cinnamon French Toast with Warm Apple Sauce

Spicy Hot Chocolate

Comfort foods are usually foods from our childhood, reminding us of days tucked up in front of the television, a blanket wrapped around us. They somehow can be appealing and satisfying when no other foods can. These are recipes to turn to when you know you need to eat and don't know what you want. They are healthy, simple and tasty.

CHAI TEA

Serves 2

500 ml water

¾ tsp Darjeeling tea, loose

75 ml milk

30 g sugar

Piece of cinnamon stick, about 3-4 cm

½ tsp freshly grated ginger

½ tsp whole green cardamoms, crushed open

Simply put all the ingredients into a medium saucepan, and bring to the boil. Immediately reduce the heat so that it is barely simmering. Leave to simmer for about 20-30 minutes, and strain into warmed cups. Offer more sugar to suit.

Cardamom stimulates the stomach and aids digestion, even relieving flatulence, but is known as a cooking spice for its flavour. Cinnamon is soothing. This tea is wonderfully relaxing and great before bedtime.

If you wish to use it, decaffeinated tea is available in most supermarkets.

LASSI YOGURT DRINK

Serves 2

200 g plain low fat yogurt

125 ml cold water

1 Tbsp fresh lemon juice

1 Tbsp fresh lime juice

1 ½ Tbsp fresh orange juice

2 Tbsp castor sugar or honey

½ cup ice cubes

Simply place all the ingredients, including ice cubes into the blender. Can be served over more ice cubes in tall glasses. Simple and delicious.

Yogurt is a probiotic food, beneficial to reinforce the intestines with 'friendly' bacteria, which aids digestion and absorption of foods.

All citrus fruits are an excellent source of vitamin C. Oranges also have strong anti inflammatory effects, which can help improve digestion also.

This lassi is a soothing drink in hot weather.

SMOKEY TOMATO AND BACON SOUP

Serves 4

---

2 Tbsp olive oil

2 medium onions, finely chopped

100 g piece smoky bacon, cut into
3 or 4 pieces

3 x 400 g cans of tomatoes (or approx
12 large ripe tomatoes, roughly chopped)

2 Tbsp tomato puree

2 Tbsp chopped fresh parsley

Salt and freshly ground black pepper

Heat the oil in a large pan. Add the onions
and chunks of bacon and cook for about
5 minutes, stirring occasionally, or until
the onions have softened and the bacon
is lightly golden.

Stir the tomatoes and the tomato puree
into the pan. Bring to a simmer, and cook
gently for 10-15 minutes, until all the flavours
are combined.

This soup can be served chunky, just as
it is. Lift the bacon chunks out and chop
them roughly. Blend the soup in a blender or
food processor if desired. Blending half and
leaving half textured also works well.

Season to taste.

Ladle the soup into warmed bowls, and
garnish with the chopped parsley and
chopped bacon.

Serve at once.

*For a vegetarian version, simply omit the
bacon. Some toast or crusty rolls goes well
with the soup.*

SALMON AND LEEK TART

Serves 4-6

---

1 x 20 cm/8" savoury pastry shell, pre-baked

25 g unsalted butter

75 ml water

150 g leeks, thinly sliced

150 g cooked salmon, flaked

2 eggs

2 egg yolks

230 ml whipping cream

2 Tbsp tomato ketchup

1 Tbsp chopped fresh herbs such as parsley, tarragon, chives or basil

¼ tsp salt

Pinch of white pepper

Preheat the temperature to 170°C.

To cook the leeks, melt the butter in a pan with the water and salt. Add the leeks and fry gently for about 4-5 minutes until just cooked. Allow the leeks to cool slightly, then squeeze out the excess liquid. Toss the flaked salmon with the leeks. Cover the bottom of the baked pastry with the mix.

In a medium bowl, whisk together the eggs and egg yolks until well blended. Add the remaining ingredients and whisk gently until the mixture is smooth. Gently pour the filling into the tart base, over the salmon and leeks, and cook in the preheated oven for about 30 minutes, or until the tart is completely set.

Allow to cool slightly before serving.

This can be served hot or warm.

Tarts like this can be appealing when nothing else is. They can also be prepared ahead of time and eaten cold. A salad is a perfect partner.

VEGETABLE FRITTATA

Serves 4

2 Tbsp oil

1 red onion diced

2 red/green/yellow peppers, diced

1 clove garlic, crushed

6 eggs

2 medium tomatoes, diced

100 g feta or goat's cheese, crumbled

3 Tbsp flat leaf parsley chopped

Salt and freshly ground black pepper

In a large heavy based fry pan, heat the oil over medium heat, and cook the onion and peppers until soft, approx 8 minutes. Add the garlic and cook a further minute.

Break the eggs in a bowl, season well with salt and pepper, and stir until well mixed. Tip into the fry pan, along with the diced tomato. Turn the heat down to low and use a spatula to keep moving the mixture around so the eggs are cooking evenly. When they are starting to set, add the crumbled cheese and parsley. Stir them through evenly and let the mix now set into a' pattie'.

The frittata can be finished cooking in two ways. The first way is to let the 'pattie' cook and firm up for a couple of minutes. It will be a golden brown on the bottom. Carefully flip onto a plate, and slide back into the fry pan so that the other side can now brown. The second way is to set under a medium grill and cook for approx 10 minutes. The frittata will be cooked golden and be firm. Cut into wedges. Serve with a spoonful of salsa. A salad would be a balanced accompaniment.

Any leftover vegetables can be used up instead of the peppers and tomato. Cooked potato diced is traditional in a 'Spanish omelette'. Green beans or broccoli work well.

BASIL PESTO MACARONI AND CHEESE

Serves 3-4

---

30 g butter

2 Tbsp flour

250 ml / 1 cup hot milk

Salt and pepper

250 g macaroni, cooked to packet instructions and drained, still hot

100 g cheddar cheese, grated

100 g parmesan, grated

3 Tbsp basil pesto (shop bought)

3 Tbsp fresh basil, chopped

Preheat the oven to 190°C and also preheat the grill. Lightly butter a large baking dish about 30 x 20 cm (12 x 8").

Place the butter, flour and milk into a medium saucepan. Whisk constantly over a moderate heat until it has thickened, about 5-8 minutes. Season lightly with salt and pepper.

Add half the cheese to the sauce, along with the pesto. Add the macaroni to the pan and stir together to mix well. Check and adjust seasoning to taste. Stir in the fresh basil. Tip into the greased baking dish, and sprinkle generously with the remaining cheese. Bake in a preheated oven for about 10-15 minutes. Finish under a hot grill to brown the top to a golden brown.

Macaroni and cheese is a real comfort food, reminding us of childhood. To add more flavour and make the dish more grown up, a shallot, finely minced and a crushed clove of garlic can be added to the white sauce mix (first 3 ingredients) as it is being cooked .

CHICKEN AND BARLEY SOUP

Serves 4

---

1 medium onion, chopped

1 medium leek, finely chopped

½ stick celery, finely chopped

2 Tbsp olive oil

1 medium carrot, grated

2-3 cooked chicken breasts (or 2 breasts and 2 thighs), chopped

2 chicken stock cubes dissolved in 3 litres of boiling water

1 tsp salt

100 g barley

Handful fresh parsley, finely chopped

In a large saucepan, heat the oil and sauté the onion, leek and celery for approx 5 minutes. Add the carrot, chicken stock and half a tsp of salt. Simmer for about 20 minutes, until the vegetables are cooked through.

At the same time, place the barley in a small pan and cover liberally with boiling water. Cook off over medium heat for the same length of time, making sure it doesn't boil dry.

When the barley is soft, add it and the cooked chicken and chopped parsley to the soup and simmer for a further 10 minutes to allow the flavours to blend. This soup is even better the second day.

Chicken is good for convalescence and for building general resistance; full of protein, iron and zinc.

This soup is quick to prepare.

Turkey could replace the chicken.

RISOTTO WITH ASPARAGUS, PEAS, AND EDAMAME

Serves 4

---

100 g shelled edamame (fresh or frozen)

75 g peas (fresh or frozen)

120 g asparagus tips, cut into 1 cm pieces

75 g onions, finely chopped

50 g butter

300 g Arborio or another risotto rice

1 litre chicken or vegetable stock, hot

Salt to taste

1 tsp fresh lemon zest

50 g parmesan cheese

2 Tbsp chopped basil or parsley

Cook the beans, peas, and asparagus tips in boiling salted water until just cooked. Refresh under cold water when cooked. Drain and set aside.

In a heavy based pan, gently sweat off the onions over a medium heat with 30 g of butter until soft and transparent. Stir in the Arborio rice, and stir gently for about 2 minutes. Reduce the heat and add a ladle of stock. Stir fairly continuously and wait each time until nearly all the liquid has been absorbed before adding more.

After 15-20 minutes, the rice should be cooked, and all the liquid added and absorbed. Check for seasoning, and add salt if needed.

Stir the vegetables into the rice, and cook for about 2 minutes more to heat through. Remove from the heat Add the lemon zest and parmesan and fresh herbs. Serve at once in warmed bowls.

Butternut squash works wonderfully in risotto. As an alternative to this risotto, simply peel and halve a butternut squash, scooping out the seeds. Dice the flesh and simmer in the hot stock for 10-15 minutes until tender. Retrieve with a slotted spoon and roughly mash with a potato masher. Add to the risotto instead of the green vegetables.

SCRAMBLED EGGS ON A TOASTED BAGEL AND A HERBED CREAM CHEESE

Serves 2

---

4 large free range organic eggs

1 Tbsp milk or cream

Salt and fresh ground pepper to taste

1 Tbsp butter or olive oil

For the herbed cream cheese:

2 oz/60 g cream cheese

1 Tbsp cream

1 Tbsp finely sliced spring onion (scallion)

½ Tbsp fresh parsley, finely chopped

½ Tbsp fresh thyme/tarragon/oregano or all mixed together

Salt and fresh ground black pepper

2 split bagels

Butter

Beat the cream cheese in a bowl until soft. Add the cream and herbs, and stir until smooth. Season with salt and pepper. Set aside.

Beat the eggs with the milk or cream and salt and pepper in a wide bowl until just blended. Heat a large non stick frypan over medium low heat. Add the butter and swirl to coat the bottom of the frypan. Add the egg mixture and cook slowly, stirring gently. When the eggs are just set to your liking, serve on warmed plates, either on top of, or beside freshly toasted bagels.

Top with the herbed cream cheese and serve at once.

Eggs are an amazing source of good quality protein. One of the most important substances in egg yolk is lecithin, vital to many of the body's metabolic processes. It also makes eggs an important brain food, contributing to memory and concentration.

WHOLEGRAIN BLUEBERRY PANCAKES

Serves 4

---

250 g wholewheat flour

250 g oats (rolled or flakes)

45 g demerara sugar

1 Tbsp baking powder

1 Tbsp cinnamon

Dash of salt

2 eggs

350 ml soy, almond or rice milk

45 g canola or vegetable oil

1 Tbsp vanilla essence

1 punnet blueberries
(or approx 200 g frozen blueberries)

Vegetable oil for cooking the pancakes

Stir the dry ingredients together in a large mixing bowl. Mix together the eggs, milk, oil and vanilla.

Pour the wet mixture into the dry, stir lightly with a wooden spoon until just mixed, do not over mix. If batter is too thick add a little more milk. Toss in the blueberries, and spread them through the batter.

Heat a large heavy bottomed saucepan over medium heat and pour a splash of oil just to evenly coat the bottom of the pan. Spoon in the batter, approx 4 pancakes, depending on the size of the pan. Cook out over medium heat, allowing bubbles to form on top and the edges to turn golden brown; approx 3-4 minutes. Turn over and cook for a further 1-2 minutes.

Serve with maple syrup.

Pancakes for breakfast brings out the child in all of us. White flour will work perfectly well, as will cow's milk.

CINNAMON FRENCH TOAST WITH WARM APPLE SAUCE

Serves 2

---

2 eggs

Pinch of salt

1 Tbsp water

4 slices thickly sliced bread

1 Tbsp butter

Ground cinnamon

Good quality apple sauce, warm

Combine the eggs, salt and water and stir until frothy. Heat a heavy based fry pan over medium high heat. Dip 2 of the slices of bread into the egg, letting it soak a little on each side. Melt half of the butter in the hot pan, and fry the bread until lightly brown on each side. Remove from heat and sprinkle with cinnamon. Repeat with the slices of bread and serve with the warmed apple sauce.

A sweet breakfast that is comforting and filling.

SPICY HOT CHOCOLATE

Serves 2

---

2 Cups semi skimmed milk or soya milk

Good pinch of ground nutmeg

Good pinch cinnamon

Good pinch of cayenne pepper

5 Tbsp good quality dark chocolate, grated or finely chopped

Place milk and spices in a saucepan over a medium heat and bring just to the boil. Allow to cool slightly. This allows the spices to infuse into the milk. Whisk in the grated chocolate and sweeten with a little honey or sugar if desired. Can be frothed with a whisk or blitzer. Serve at once.

Buy a good quality drinking chocolate and substitute for the dark chocolate!

CALORIE
BOOSTERS

CALORIE BOOSTERS

Baked Four Cheese Pasta

Chicken with Tagliatelle, Mushrooms and Cream

Toasted Bacon and Egg Mayonnaise Sandwich

Warm Potato and Cheddar Flan

Cod Fish Pie

Hearty Chicken Casserole

Most of these recipes have cream and/or butter in fairly substantial quantities.
The higher fat and calorie content will help those who need to put weight back on.
Dairy is credited for helping growth, strong bones and convalescence too. So even
if weight gain is not an issue, small portions of these dishes, served with a salad or a
portion of freshly steamed vegetables may be a healthy pleasure for anyone.

BAKED FOUR CHEESE PASTA

Serves 4-6

---

450 g dried macaroni, or penne

100 g butter

4 Tbsp light olive oil

200 g tender young spinach leaves

350 g button mushrooms, quartered

2 Tbsp plain flour

500 ml milk

300 ml double cream

100 g blue cheese, crumbled

100 g cheddar, grated

100 g mozzarella, grated

100 g parmesan or pecorino, grated

Salt and freshly ground black pepper

Preheat the oven to 190°C.

Grease a large oven proof baking dish. Bring a large pan of salted water to the boil, and cook the pasta according to the packet's instructions. Drain and set aside in the large pan.

Heat 30 g of the butter and half of the oil in a large fry pan over high heat. Add the spinach, season generously, and cook for 2-4 minutes, stirring occasionally, until wilted. Tip into a sieve set over a bowl. When the spinach has cooled a little, squeeze out any excess liquid gently, using your hands.

Place 30 g of the butter and oil in the large fry pan over a medium heat, and cook the mushrooms off over a high heat for 2-3 minutes. Season with salt.

To make the white sauce, place the remaining butter in a medium sauce pan with the flour and milk, and bring to the boil, whisking constantly. Reduce the heat and cook, stirring frequently, for 5-10 minutes, until the sauce is smooth and thickened. Season to taste, and stir in the cream. Add the spinach, mushrooms, white sauce, and 2 thirds of the cheeses to the pasta. Toss well until combined. Check for seasoning one last time.

Tip into a lightly greased baking dish. Top with the remaining cheeses. Bake for 15-20 minutes until bubbling and lightly golden. Serve with a salad.

To simplify, leave out the vegetables. If it sounds too rich, the cream may be omitted and more milk used instead. A bought white sauce would help make the recipe faster and easier.

CHICKEN WITH TAGLIATELLE, MUSHROOMS AND CREAM

Serves 2

2 skinned boned chicken breasts

2 Tbsp olive oil

Salt and pepper

1 small white onion, finely chopped

100 g sliced mushrooms
(button, chanterelle, brown cap)

1 Tbsp olive oil

125 ml single cream

100 ml chicken stock, optional

Salt and white pepper

Tagliatelle pasta, cooked to
packet instructions

Cut the chicken breasts into bite sized pieces. Season lightly with salt and pepper. Heat 2 Tbsp of olive oil in a large frying pan and sauté the chicken pieces until cooked through. Remove from heat.

Sauté the onion and mushrooms in the remaining oil, in another frying pan over medium heat for approx 3-5 minutes. Add the cream, chicken stock, salt and pepper, and simmer gently until it has reached a sauce consistency. Place the chicken pieces in just at the end, to warm through.

Place the hot pasta on a plate and ladle the chicken sauce over liberally. Serve at once.

Optional: a little dried, crushed porcini or other dried mushroom added to the sauce as it is simmers will greatly enhance the flavour.

Any pasta can be substituted for the tagliatelle.

Store bought cooked chicken pieces could easily be substituted to cut down on cooking time.

TOASTED BACON AND EGG MAYONNAISE SANDWICH

Serves 2

150-200 g back bacon, cooked and warm (approx ¾ -1 package)

Several leaves of Iceberg lettuce, can be shredded, or left whole

1-2 tomatoes, sliced

2 eggs

2-3 Tbsp good quality store bought mayonnaise

Wholegrain or whole wheat bread, sliced, and lightly toasted

Salt and freshly ground black pepper

For the eggs mayonnaise:

To hard boil the eggs, cover eggs with cold water, and bring to the boil. Reduce heat, and simmer for 8 minutes. Drain eggs, and crack the shells and refresh in cold water to stop the cooking.

Roughly chop the hard boiled eggs. Season with salt and pepper. Gently fold in enough mayonnaise to bind.

Lightly toast the bread and butter. Spread with the egg mayonnaise. Top with the sliced tomatoes, the cooked back bacon, and finish with the lettuce. Season with salt and freshly ground pepper. Top with the second piece of toast. Cut in half and serve warm.

Add slices of avocado or cooked chicken to make a heartier sandwich that can be a meal in itself. Avocados are considered a cancer protective food, full of oleic acid – a powerful antioxidant food.

WARM POTATO AND CHEDDAR FLAN

Serves 4

---

200 g potatoes, peeled and roughly cut

125 ml milk

125 ml whipping cream

150 g mature cheddar, crumbled

3 egg yolks

Salt and pepper

1 Tbsp butter, softened

Preheat the oven to 160°C.

Cook the potatoes in salted boiling water until just tender. Drain and return to the pan with the milk and cream. Simmer for 4-5 minutes, until the liquid thickens slightly.

Remove from the heat and mash with a potato masher. Season with salt and pepper and allow to cool for a few minutes before stirring in the cheddar cheese and egg yolks.

Generously butter 4-6 ramekins, 4 x 150 ml (5 fl oz) size or oven proof cups, etc. Pour or ladle the potato and cheese mixture into the moulds, and cover with foil.

Place an oven dish in the oven and pour in some boiling water to make a water bath (a bain marie).

Place the ramekins in the water bath, and bake for 30 minutes, or until just set. Remove from the oven, and allow to cool for 15-20 minutes before serving.

Lovely served with rustic bread or toasted focaccia.

These are actually very simple to make. Goat's cheese works really well also and has a slightly tangy flavour.

COD FISH PIE

Serves 2

---

25 g unsalted butter

1 small leek, thinly sliced

80 g button mushrooms, sliced

1 large potato, thinly sliced

4 eggs

150 ml single cream

1½ Tbsp chopped fresh dill
(or 1-2 tsp dried)

300g skinless, boneless cod fillet,
cut into 2 cm pieces

50 g cheddar, grated

Preheat the oven to 220°C.

If using a microwave to begin, place the butter, leek slices, button mushrooms and then add the potato in an even layer into a rectangular, 5cm deep, microwave and ovenproof dish. Season generously, and add a splash of water. Cover with non PVC plastic film, and pierce a couple of times with a knife. Microwave on high for 5 minutes, or until the potatoes are done.

If you don't have a microwave, melt the butter in a large pan. Add the leeks and sauté until softened, then add the mushrooms and cook for a further minute.

Transfer to an ovenproof dish.

Cook the potatoes in a pan of boiling salted water for 8-10 minutes, or until just tender, then drain, and layer over the leeks and mushrooms.

Place the eggs and milk in a jug, and beat until combined. Add the dill and season with salt and pepper generously.

Scatter the fish on top of the potato mixture, season it with salt, and pour over the egg mixture, stirring slightly. Place in the oven for 5 minutes. Remove from the oven, sprinkle over the cheese, then return to the oven for about 10 minutes.

To finish, preheat the grill to hot, and place the dish underneath until the cheese is bubbling and golden.

The World Health Organisation's Food Pyramid advises eating fish a few times each week. It contains plenty of proteins and is good for almost everyone.

Other white fish could be substituted for the cod. Buy what is freshest.

HEARTY CHICKEN CASSEROLE

Serves 4

---

675 g (1 lb 8 oz) boneless, skinless chicken breasts

Salt and pepper

28 g (1 oz) butter

1 Tbsp light olive oil

1 small onion, finely sliced

125 g (4 oz) mushrooms, finely sliced

2 Tbsp tomato paste

250 ml (8 fl oz) chicken or beef stock, from cubes

Several drops of Tabasco sauce or dash of paprika (optional)

125 ml (4 fl oz) sour cream

Slice the chicken breasts in to 2 cm / ¾ inch strips. Season with salt and pepper.

Heat the butter and oil in a frying pan until foaming. Add half of the chicken strips, and saute over high heat for 4-5 minutes, until just cooked and lightly browned. Remove the cooked strips, to a warm dish, and saute the remaining chicken pieces. When the chicken is completely cooked, remove and then saute the mushrooms and onions with a little salt and pepper.

When the onions are soft, remove the vegetables from the pan, add the tomato paste to the pan, and fry briefly, then add the stock and the sour cream. Boil until it thickens slightly, and then add the chicken and the vegetables back to the pan. Simmer for 5-10 minutes.

Serve with potatoes, noodles, or rice.

As well as protein, chicken provides easily absorbed iron and zinc, making it beneficial as a general resistance builder. Chicken has long been known as a convalescence food.

VEGGIE

VEGGIE

Indian Pilau Rice

Spicy Vegetarian Chilli with Sweet Potato

Quick Vegetable Stir-fry

Roast Red Peppers Stuffed with Jalapeno and Cheddar Cheese

Spaghetti with Tomato, Chickpeas and Basil

Carrot, Apple, Beetroot and Ginger Juice

Mango and Passionfruit Smoothie

Spiced Butternut Squash Soup

Dressings

Vegetables are renowned for their vitamin and mineral content and have a protective role in diet. Keeping them raw such as in salads and juices is good insurance that their constituents will be retained. Eating vegetarian is also known to be easier on the digestive system. At times of constipation (a common side effect caused by pain relieving medications) eating some of these high fibre recipes may help to free you up. They are all simple and totally satisfying enough, no fowl or fish or meat is needed.

INDIAN PILAU RICE

Serves 4

---

100 g (1 medium) onion, finely chopped

4 Tbsp (60 g) good quality olive oil

½ cinnamon stick

5 cardamom pods,

2-4 curry leaves (or ½ bay leaf)

1 Tbsp finely chopped fresh ginger

2 tsp medium curry powder

1 tsp turmeric powder

225 g (½ lb) Basmati rice

800 ml boiling water with 1 vegetable stock cube

Grated zest of ½ lemon

Salt

50 g (2 oz) pine nuts, lightly toasted

Fresh coriander leaves, chopped, to serve

In a large heavy-based ovenproof pan, sweat the onions in the oil over a medium heat for about 5 minutes until they are soft and transparent. Add the cinnamon, cardamom, curry/bay leaf, ginger, curry powder and tumeric and sweat gently for another minute.

Add the rice and hot vegetable stock. Bring to the boil over a medium to high heat. Cover with a tight-fitting lid and reduce heat to low. Leave to simmer for 10 minutes, and then take off the heat. Stir in the lemon zest. Replace the cover and leave the rice to steam in its own heat for 5-10 minutes. Just before serving, garnish with the toasted pine nuts and fresh coriander.

This rice is delicious the second day. Store the leftovers in a covered container in the fridge, simply reheat in the microwave and serve.

SPICY VEGETARIAN CHILLI WITH SWEET POTATO

Serves 4-6

3 Tbsp olive oil

2 medium onions, roughly chopped

2 sweet potatoes, peeled and roughly chopped

5 cloves garlic, pressed

2 red chillies, seeded and roughly chopped

1 Tbsp cumin

1 tsp chilli pepper (optional)

1 Tbsp dried oregano

½ tsp salt

1 tin black beans, rinsed and drained (400 g)

1 tin kidney beans, rinsed and drained (400 g)

3 tins chopped tomatoes (400 g each)

2 Tbsp smoky ketchup or chipotle chilli sauce

100 g fresh or frozen corn or ½ small tin

Optional
to garnish:

60 ml sour cream
(or full fat greek yoghurt)

½ tsp cinnamon

Freshly chopped coriander

Heat oil in a large pan over medium heat. Saute the onions and sweet potatoes until lightly browned, turning frequently. Add garlic, fresh chilli and spices. Stir into the vegetables and cook for a further 5 minutes.

Add the beans, tinned tomatoes and smoky ketchup and salt . Bring to the boil then simmer gently for 30 minutes. Add the corn in the last five minutes, just to heat through. Serve with the cinnamon laced sour cream/yoghurt and sprinkled with fresh coriander.

Chilli is one of those dishes that sometimes taste better the second day, having the flavours infuse and settle together overnight in the fridge. This chilli will freeze well.

QUICK VEGETABLE STIR-FRY

Serves 2

---

2 cloves garlic, crushed

2 cm piece fresh ginger, peeled and finely chopped

2 spring onions (or 1 medium white onion) sliced

1 red chilli, halved, seeded and sliced (optional)

100 g mange tout, sliced into bite sized length on the angle

100 g asparagus, sliced into bite sized length on the angle (if fat spears, halve lengthwise first)

50 g mushrooms (white, brown oyster or shitake), sliced

½ red pepper, sliced

100 g broccoli, cut into small florets

2 Tbsp olive or vegetable oil

1-2 Tbsp soy sauce

1-2 tsp sesame oil

Toasted sesame seeds to sprinkle over

Heat a heavy based frying pan, or wok until it is hot. Add the oil, garlic, ginger, chilli if using and spring onion. Stir for about 10 seconds and then add the rest of the vegetables. Keep tossing the mixture over high heat for a further few minutes. When the vegetables are just cooked, remove from heat and add the soy sauce and sesame oil.

Serve at once and sprinkle with toasted sesame seeds. Serve with rice or Asian noodles.

Feel free to substitute other vegetables if preferred; green beans, sweetcorn, or cabbage. All work well.

ROAST RED PEPPERS STUFFED WITH JALAPENO AND CHEDDAR CHEESE

Serves 2

2 red peppers

1 Tbsp vegetable oil

For the stuffing:

8 heaped Tbsp cooked rice

4 spring onions, finely sliced

1 red pepper, finely diced

2 garlic cloves, crushed

1-2 Tbsp sliced jalapenos, pickled or fresh (optional)

150 g mild cheddar cheese grated

Salt and freshly ground black pepper

Preheat the oven to 190°C and the grill to high.

Rub the peppers with a little vegetable oil, and roast over an open flame, or under a hot grill until they are blistered on the surface, and quite black. Allow the peppers to cool slightly, and then peel, or rub off the blackened skin. Cut the peppers in half lengthwise by starting at the stem, cutting through it, and then follow on down. This gives two attractive halves. Scoop out the seeds, and discard.

In a bowl, mix together all the stuffing ingredients, reserving 4 Tbsp of the cheese for the top. Stuff the peppers generously, and then top with the remaining cheese.

Bake in a hot oven for about 10-15 minutes (if there is top heat, i.e. a combi oven, then this is preferred) until it is golden brown, and hot through.

This is a delicious way to use up left over rice. It doesn't take long to roast the peppers, so don't be put off by the process. It is worth it.

SPAGHETTI WITH TOMATO, CHICKPEAS AND BASIL

Serves 2

½ packet of spaghetti, cooked to packet's instructions

1 large jar (650 g) tomato chilli pasta sauce

1 can (400 g) organic chickpeas, drained and rinsed

1 small handful fresh basil leaves, torn

8 Tbsp fresh chilli garlic oil
(optional, see below)

Parmesan cheese, freshly grated, to garnish (optional)

For the Chilli garlic oil:

4 medium red chillies, freshly chopped seeds and all

8 cloves garlic, crushed and finely chopped

Salt and freshly ground black pepper

150 ml extra virgin olive oil

To make the chilli garlic oil, mix the chillies with the garlic and a little salt and pepper with 2 Tbsp of the olive oil. Microwave on high for 1 minute, then remove carefully and add the remaining oil. This will keep well for approx 1 month if kept in the fridge.

While the spaghetti is cooking warm the tomato sauce with the drained chickpeas and any other vegetables that you are adding and basil. Bring it to a simmer. Drain the spaghetti. To serve, place the spaghetti in warmed serving bowls, top with the sauce, some Parmesan, if using and as much of the chilli garlic oil as you like.

Other additional ingredients to add:

Chopped black olives

Chopped sundried tomatoes

Cooked broccoli, courgette, or spinach

Cooked artichoke hearts

CARROT, APPLE, BEETROOT AND GINGER JUICE

Serves 2

---

3 medium carrots, peeled

2 medium apples, quartered

2 medium raw beets, peeled and quartered

A knob of fresh ginger (about 2 Tbsp), peeled

Feed the fruit and vegetables through a juicer, saving a carrot to finish pushing the ginger through. Stir the juice and serve immediately.

Fresh fruit and vegetable juices are very good for you; natural and full of all the benefits of the raw ingredients.

Carrots are an anti-aging food, high in beta carotene.

Beets are full of essential vitamins for healthy cells and recovering from debilitating illnesses.

They are full of various anti-carcinogens and are a good source of folate and rich in potassium.

MANGO AND PASSIONFRUIT SMOOTHIE

Serves 2

---

1 ripe mango, quartered and skinned, and chopped, or approx 1 cup frozen mango pieces

2 bananas, roughly sliced

3 passionfruit, halved

100 ml apple juice

Juice of 1 orange, or 100 ml orange juice

Juice of 1 lime

Place the juices first into the blender. Add the chopped mango, banana and the flesh and juice of the passionfruit. Blend until smooth.

Remove the seeds of the passionfruit by passing the flesh through a fine sieve as you add the juice to the blender. The seeds will discolour the smoothie. Using store bought orange and passionfruit juice is a great substitute for the fresh orange and passionfruits.

SPICED BUTTERNUT SQUASH SOUP

Serves 4-6

4 Tbsp olive oil

1 butternut squash, (approx 700-750 g) peeled, seeded and chopped

3 medium parsnips, peeled, and roughly chopped

2 medium onions, chopped

4 cloves garlic, chopped

2 Tbsp fresh ginger, chopped

1 Tbsp curry powder, optional

½-1 fresh chilli, chopped, optional or ½-1 tsp chilli powder

2 litres boiling water with 2 vegetable stock cubes

Salt and freshly ground white pepper

Heat half the oil in a large heavy frying pan over moderate heat, and add the butternut squash and the parsnip. Fry until tender, stirring occasionally, approx 8 minutes, allowing it to brown. Meanwhile sauté off the onion, garlic, ginger in the rest of the oil in a large saucepan for approx five minutes, until soft. Add the spices and chilli, if using, and stir together for a minute and then add the cooked butternut squash and parsnip.

Add the vegetable stock and bring to the boil. Reduce heat to low and simmer for approx 20-30 minutes. The squash should be very soft. Puree in a blender or with a blitzer. Taste for seasoning, and adjust salt if needed. This can be made ahead, and gently reheated. To serve, ladle into warm bowls. This is great served with nan bread.

Sweet potato can replace the parsnips.

Squashes can benefit the stomach, reducing inflammations and improving circulation. This soup is certainly a soothing meal.

MINT PESTO

Makes approx 250 ml

---

2 garlic cloves peeled and crushed

100 g toasted almonds

½ tsp salt

Large handful of fresh mint leaves

75 ml extra virgin olive oil

Place the garlic, almonds, and salt in a food processor and pulse until the almonds are quite pureed. Add the mint leaves and pulse until the mint is finely minced and blended into the almond mixture. With the machine on, slowly pour the oil in until the pesto is blended into a loose paste.

This can be kept in a covered container in the fridge until ready to use.

LEMON TAHINI DRESSING

Makes 160 ml

---

2 cloves garlic, pureed through a garlic press

1 tsp sea salt

½-1 tsp freshly ground black pepper

Juice of 1 lemon

2-3 Tbsp tahini

100 ml extra virgin olive oil

Place all ingredients except the oil in a blender or food processor. Then with the machine running, slowly pour in the oil, allowing it to emulsify.

Keep in fridge until use.

Delicious on steamed green vegetables. Tahini (sesame paste) is packed with calcium and essential fatty acids. Fresh sesame seeds can be sprinkled over dressed greens.

MISO DRESSING

Makes approx 250 ml

---

180 ml miso paste

3 Tbsp honey

3 Tbsp rice vinegar

3 Tbsp hot water

1 Tbsp sesame oil

Soy sauce to taste

Simply stir all of the ingredients together until smooth. Keep in fridge until use.

Miso pastes vary in flavour. Read the packet to see if the soybeans have been fermented with rice, or barley, and if it is salty or sweet.

CREAMY FRESH CORIANDER DRESSING

Makes approx 250 ml

---

200 ml plain yoghurt (can be low fat)

50 ml water

2 Tbsp honey

2 Tbsp lemon juice

1 tsp fresh ginger, grated or finely chopped

1 clove garlic, crushed

Pinch turmeric

Pinch ground coriander

Salt and pepper

½ bunch fresh coriander leaves, finely chopped

Combine all of the ingredients together in a bowl and mix well. Let the flavours infuse for at least 15 minutes before using. Keep in the fridge.

This is a variation of raita, an Indian mixture of yoghurt and various spices, herbs and or vegetables.

SIMPLE BALSAMIC AND OLIVE OIL DRESSING

Makes approx 250 ml

---

125 ml balsamic vinegar

125 ml extra virgin olive oil

¼ tsp salt

¼ tsp pepper

Combine all of the ingredients in a jar and shake well. Adjust salt and pepper as needed.

A peeled clove of garlic placed in the jar will infuse the vinaigrette without being too overpowering.

SWEET THINGS

Peanut Butter Cookies with Chunky Almonds

Poppyseed Cake

Baked Chocolate Brownies

Fresh Exotic Fruit with Coconut Yoghurt Cream

Banana Cinnamon Oatmeal Muffins

Date and Pecan Bar

Lemon Ricotta Cheesecake with Fresh Strawberries

Rhubarb Apple Crumble

Stuffed Baked Pear

Healthy Refrigerator Brownie

Sweet dishes are mostly thought of as an after dinner treat, however these sweet things lend themselves to any time of the day. Several of them are suitable for breakfast, especially alongside a fruit smoothie. Some are a comforting accompaniment to an afternoon tea or just a tasty snack for those who find it difficult to eat very much at a time. A little can go a long way towards satisfaction.

PEANUT BUTTER COOKIE WITH CHUNKY ALMONDS

Makes approx 2 dozen

---

100 g unsalted butter	2 eggs, stirred together
150 g smooth peanut butter	325 g plain flour
100 g caster sugar	1 tsp baking soda
100 g dark brown sugar	50 g toasted almonds, roughly chopped

Place the butter and peanut butter in mixing bowl, and with electric mixer on low speed, beat until well mixed. Add the sugars and blend in on medium speed. Scrape down the bowl, and again, on low speed, blend in the eggs, a bit at a time. Sift the baking soda and flour together, and fold into the mix, do not over mix. Place in the fridge to chill for 1-2 hours.

Preheat oven to 180°C.

Have 2-3 pre-greased or non stick baking trays.

Take cookie dough from fridge, and roll into small balls (approx 1 ½ "). Place on greased or non stick baking trays, leaving a good 2 " between each ball.

Place 3 Tbsp granulated sugar on a saucer. Using a fork, dip the fork into the sugar and then use it to slightly flatten a cookie ball. Press once and then turn the fork 90° and press again, in a criss cross fashion. Continue to dip the fork into sugar each time, and press out the rest of the cookies. Sprinkle each cookie with a few of the toasted almonds.

Bake for 10-15 minutes, until light brown. Remove from oven and cool for a minute on the tray to set before removing to a wire rack.

Wonderful warm, but once cooled can be stored in an airtight container. A big scoop of Nutella could be added to the cookie dough to give a wonderful hazelnut flavour. Toasted chopped hazelnuts could be used to top this version.

POPPYSEED CAKE

Serves 6

---

125 g unsalted butter

375 g sugar

2 eggs

350 g plain flour

1 ½ tsp baking soda

125 ml sour cream

200 ml water

Juice of 1 orange, approx 50 ml

125 g white chocolate, finely chopped or grated

125 g poppy seeds

1 Tbsp freshly grated orange zest

1 x 20 cm springform cake tin or a loaf tin.

Preheat Oven 170°C.

Cream the butter and sugar to light and fluffy in a mixer. Lower the speed and add the eggs slowly, allowing them to be blended into the butter/sugar mix before adding more.
(Tip: A handful of the flour mix added here helps to keep the mix from splitting.)

Sift the dry ingredients together. Stir the liquids together separately. On the lowest speed, add sifted dry alternatively with the liquids to the cake mixture. Dust the white chocolate lightly with flour. This prevents it from sinking to the bottom of the batter during baking. Lastly fold in white chocolate, poppy seeds and orange zest.

Grease and flour the spring form cake tin.

Pour the cake mixture into the tin and place in the centre of the preheated oven.

Bake for 1-1½ hours. When a toothpick inserted in the centre of cake comes out clean, the cake is done.

Remove from oven. Carefully release the sides of the cake from the sides of the tin with a knife, and allow to cool. Remove from the tin and set on a plate when cool.

When cool glaze with following glaze:

60 g white chocolate, melted over just simmering water, 2 tbsp orange juice,

1 cup icing sugar, sifted.

The consistency of the glaze should not be too runny. It will set on the cake as the chocolate sets.

This moist cake will keep well, simply cover with cling film and store in a cool and dry place. Great for a sweet bite after a meal or with a cup of tea.

BAKED CHOCOLATE BROWNIES

Fills a 20 cm x 20 cm baking tin

150 g dark chocolate, melted

90 g / 6 Tbsp unsalted butter, melted

4 Tbsp golden syrup

2 eggs

1 ½ tsp vanilla essence

90 g plain flour

150 g icing sugar

2 tsp baking powder

20 g cocoa powder

Optional Extras

120 g white chocolate chips or

120 g dark chocolate chips or

Some little marshmallows

A couple handfuls lightly toasted and chopped pecans or hazelnuts

Preheat oven to 170°C.

Grease baking tin. Set aside.

Stir the melted chocolate together with the melted butter until well blended. Next stir in the golden syrup, followed by the eggs, one at a time, and the vanilla extract. Stir well to ensure all the ingredients are well incorporated together.

Sift together all of the dry ingredients, and fold this into the above mix. Lastly, fold in the chocolate chips, and/or nuts, if using. Do not over stir, just mix gently until evenly mixed.

Pour into the greased baking tin, and place in the centre of the oven. Bake for 25-30 minutes. The edges will be crisp and pulling away from the edges of the pan.

The middle should be quite firm, and bounce back if pressed lightly with the tip of a finger. A toothpick inserted into the centre should come out clean. If you like your brownies slightly gooey in the centre, reduce cooking time to 20-22 minutes. The toothpick will be coated but warm to the touch.

Remove from oven and leave to cool for 5-10 minutes before cutting into individual size portions.

These brownies stay moist and fresh for at least a couple days if kept airtight. You could place them in an airtight container, or wrap them up individually in double layers of cling film.

FRESH EXOTIC FRUIT WITH COCONUT YOGHURT CREAM

Serves 2

1 punnet of ready chopped exotic fruit, or a selection of your own, approx 100-150 g for each person

Juice of 1 lime

100 ml coconut milk approx ¼ tin

100 ml thick-set, Greek-style yoghurt (use low fat if preferred)

1 Tbsp honey or caster sugar

1 Tbsp coconut flakes, toasted or grated fresh coconut (optional)

Place the exotic fruit into two serving bowls.

Stir the coconut milk into the yoghurt. Taste and if desired a spoonful of honey or sugar can be added.

Scoop a dollop of the yoghurt cream on to the fruit and sprinkle with toasted coconut flakes or freshly grated coconut if using.

A very simple and quick sweet that always tastes good and is light and easy to digest. You could just use mango, or papaya, or even pineapple if you preferred. Any tropical fruit goes with coconut flavour.

BANANA CINNAMON OATMEAL MUFFINS

Approx 12 muffins

---

450 ml buttermilk

150 g rolled oats (old fashioned style)

2 Tbsp melted butter

2 eggs

140 g soft brown sugar

200 g plain flour

2 tsp ground cinnamon

1 tsp baking soda

Salt

Zest of one small lemon

140 g mashed ripe bananas

1 tsp vanilla extract (optional)

Lightly toasted and roughly chopped almonds or hazelnuts are a nice added extra option

---

Preheat oven to 180°C.

If possible, leave the oats to soak overnight in the buttermilk. If not, aim for at least a couple hours (if overnight, cover with cling film and place in fridge).

Sift the flour, soda and salt together into a big bowl. Add in the brown sugar and lemon zest.

Stir in the oats and buttermilk mixture.

Stir in the melted butter and eggs, but only until just combined. Fold in the mashed banana and vanilla, and nuts if using.

Line 12 muffin moulds with paper liners. Fill each liner to about ¾ full and bake for about 17 to 20 minutes. Enjoy warm and fresh, or freeze for handy snacks.

It is really worth the extra effort of soaking the oats in the buttermilk overnight.

Finely diced peeled apple can replace the banana. Toss the diced apple in the lemon juice before adding both to the mixture. Ground flax or hemp can be added along with or instead of the nuts.

DATE AND PECAN BAR

Makes one 17 cm x 22 cm tray

---

250 g / 8 oz chopped dates

Enough water to generously cover
in a small pan

1 Tbsp zest of fresh orange

150 g plain flour

100 g flaked oats

90 g unsalted butter, diced and pliable

100 g golden brown sugar

Salt

½ tsp baking soda

Zest of one orange

100 g pecans, lightly toasted
and roughly chopped

Preheat the oven to 170°C.

Grease the baking tray lightly.

Place the dried dates in a small pan, and cover generously with cold water. Add half of the orange zest and place over a medium heat. Bring to a gentle boil and reduce the heat to a simmer. Cook out until soft and mushy. The length of time will be very dependent on just how dried the dates are. The amount of water will vary also, as different amounts will be absorbed for the same reason. Keep the fruits well moistened, do not allow to cook out dry. Once they are very soft, remove from heat and drain the excess liquid. Allow to cool and roughly chop.

Sift the flour, salt and soda into the oats. Add the sugar, remaining zest and half the chopped pecans and mix well. Add the butter, and work with your fingertips. Pat half of this mix in to the bottom of the baking tray, and fold the rest together with the chopped dates. Pat this on to the top of the mix in the baking tray, and sprinkle with the remaining pecans.

Place in a preheated oven for approx 25 minutes, until golden. Remove from the oven and allow to cool. Cut into squares and store in an airtight container. These will keep for a few days.

These can be a very healthy start to the day, a high energy snack, or simply a tasty sweet. They would be delicious served with a scoop of ice cream

LEMON RICOTTA CHEESECAKE WITH FRESH STRAWBERRIES

Serves 6-8

For the tart

20-23 cm pre-baked pie shell

400 g / 14 oz ricotta, drained

4 egg yolks

175 g / 6 oz caster sugar

1 tsp vanilla essence

Juice and zest of 2 lemons

25 g / 1 oz flour, sifted

For the sauce

450 g / 1 lb fresh strawberries, hulled and halved or quartered

55 g / 2oz caster sugar

1 Tbsp lemon juice

Pre-heat the oven to 180°C.

Drain the ricotta by lining a sieve with a clean tea-towel and allowing it to drain through for at least 1 hour. (If the excess liquid is not removed, the tart can end up rather watery.) Meanwhile, whisk together the egg yolks and caster sugar until pale and fluffy.

Add the vanilla and lemon juice and zest. Add the drained ricotta and the sifted flour. Mix gently but thoroughly. Pour the mixture into the pre-baked tart shell and bake in pre-heated oven for about 20-25 minutes until the centre of the tart just wobbles very slightly. Set aside to cool.

For the sauce, puree half of the strawberries in a blender with the caster sugar and lemon juice then pass sauce through a sieve. Toss the remaining strawberries into the sauce.

To serve, slice the tart into wedges and place in the centre of each plate with some strawberries and a little sauce.

This delicious light creamy tart is not as sweet or rich as a classic cheesecake.

If preferred, cream cheese can be used. It does not need drained first. Place it and the sugar into a mixer and whisk on medium speed to soften it before adding the egg yolks. Because it is a firmer consistency a mixer is needed for this option. The rest of the recipe can stay the same.

RHUBARB APPLE CRUMBLE

Serves 4

450 g / 1 lb fresh rhubarb

2 medium apples

Juice of 1 small lemon

60-90 g / 4-6 Tbsp sugar

For the crumble

50 g white sugar

50 g golden brown sugar

100 g plain flour

75 g unsalted butter, diced

Zest of one small lemon

75 g toasted, roughly chopped almonds

Preheat the oven to 180°C.

To prepare the filling, top and tail the rhubarb, and lightly peel the stringy sides. Chop into bit size pieces. Core and peel the apple, chop into bite size pieces and toss in the lemon juice to avoid discolouration. Place the fruits in a medium pan, over a medium heat, and cook along with the lemon juice and the sugar, until the fruits are just tender, about 5 minutes. Drain through a colander.

Place all the ingredients for the crumble in a medium bowl, and, using your fingers, work together until you have nice chunky bits, a pea pod like consistency. This can be done in a food processor.

Place the cooked fruit in an oven proof dish, and cover evenly and generously with the crumble topping. Place in a pre-heated oven and bake for 30 minutes. Remove from oven. This can be served warm or at room temperature.

Pear can be substituted for the rhubarb in the winter months. And sundried fruit such as cherries or blueberries are a wonderful addition at any time. A handful of flaked oats can be added to the crumble topping for a heartier version.

STUFFED BAKED PEAR

Serves 2

---

1 ripe pear

Juice of ½ lemon

2 tsp clear honey

50 g natural yoghurt
(Greek is richer or use natural or low fat)

For the filling (enough for 4-6 portions)

25 g / 1 oz whole almonds,
toasted and chopped

25 g / 1 oz amaretti or ginger biscuits

25 / 1 Tbsp unsalted butter, room temp.

15 g sugar / 1 Tbsp

Preheat the oven to 190°C.

Make the filling first.

Crush the amaretti or ginger biscuits. Roughly mix with the almonds, butter and sugar.

Peel the pear, and roll in the lemon juice to avoid discolouration. Halve the pear length wise, and core. Pack half of the filling on to each pear half, this should fill the cavity and cover most of the exposed half.

Place the halves in an oven proof dish and bake in the preheated oven for approx 15 minutes, depending on the ripeness and variety of the pear. It is cooked when the tip of a knife pierces the centre easily.

To serve, stir the honey into the yoghurt. Place a warm pear half on each plate, and scoop a dollop of yogurt beside it.

This recipe works equally well with peaches or apricots.

This is a quick and easy sweet to whip up at a moment's notice.

HEALTHY REFRIGERATOR BROWNIE

Serves 2

---

250 g / 2 cups pitted dates, chopped

100 g / ¾ cup cocoa powder

100 g / 1 cup ground almonds

100 g / ¾ cup walnuts, roughly chopped

3 Tbsp coconut oil, melted

1 tsp vanilla essence

6-8 Tbsp desiccated coconut

Place the dates, cocoa, and ground almonds into the food processor and blend to a thick coarse powder texture, about 1 minute.

Add the walnuts, and blend for a further minute.

Drizzle in the coconut oil and vanilla and pulse for 30 seconds, until the mixture is coming together.

Sprinkle half of the desiccated coconut into the base of the baking tray, and press the brownie mix in evenly, using the back of a spoon. Sprinkle the rest of the coconut over the top. Gently cut the brownies into small square portions, leaving in place in the tray and set in the refrigerator or freezer.

Try using 2-3 plastic take away containers as a substitute for the baking tray. It allows for easy storage, especially in the freezer. Just break off a portion and eat directly from the freezer – delicious.

Pecans or macadamia nuts can be used instead of walnuts.

RESTORING WELL BEING

I have been involved with Cancer Focus Northern Ireland for some years giving a program of classes and workshops called Recovery Yoga. Yoga is a holistic healing system for bringing balance and connection to body, mind, emotions and spirit. When the balance has been disturbed by serious illness, practicing yoga can assist in a number of ways to restore it.

YOGA

bringing balance and connection to body, mind, emotions and spirit

Even when unwell you can take steps to help yourself by learning about the range of practical tools that yoga consists of. The simplest of yoga breathing, relaxation movement, and meditation techniques will have profound effects on all the systems of the body.

They can also help to manage the stress, anxiety, and pain of cancer surgery, chemotherapy and radiotherapy.

Yoga practices encourage the development of inner resources that help in dealing with a life-changing illness. The unfolding qualities of self-awareness, resilience, stability, faith, and trust enable us to meet all of life's challenges and to use them as opportunities for growth and change. My work as a yoga therapist has given me the solid belief that yoga has much to offer to people who are living with cancer, and also, the carers of people who have cancer.

THE BREATH

develop breath awareness

It is a fact that the way we breathe can profoundly influence the health of our body and our mind. Therefore, think of how helpful it can be if we can learn to use our breath as a therapy to influence and heal our physical, mental and emotional states.

Many self-care practices talk about 'being with the breath'. What does this mean? It simply means turning one's awareness to your breathing and tuning into it. Think of all the characteristics that can be observed. There is the sound, the depth, the rhythm, the length, and the temperature.

Being with the breath helps connect us back to our body and the present moment, which can help put fears and anxieties into perspective. It may then be possible to begin to nourish positive thoughts and intentions when the body/mind/spirit are in a calmer place.

It may be difficult to change a feeling, thought or attitude in the moment, but it can be possible to change the breath. The first step to changing the breath is to become aware of it. This focusing on the breath may be hard at first, and so this is why it is helpful to begin with simple breathing practices. These can be with or without movement and will help a person learn to listen, to sit with and just 'be with' their breath. They are ways to get to know your breath; to become friends and allies with it.

A full exhalation leads naturally to fuller inhalation, which brings more oxygen with its obvious good effects on health; and with its subtler effects on energy levels. Exhalation also calms the sympathetic nervous system (which initiates the 'fight or flight' response) and brings into play the parasympathetic nervous system (which gives the body and mind the message that all is well, that you can let down your guard and rest).

Exercises that lengthen the exhalation are particularly beneficial in helping the breath return to a natural state. When a person is upset in any way, their breathing usually gets much shallower. This tension, be it mental or physical, can make the body's systems not able to function optimally, so the immune system will function better when the body is freed by breathing practices. When the immune system is strengthened, our own innate healing systems will be enhanced.

BREATH AWARENESS EXERCISE

full yogic breath, or diaphragmatic breathing

Lie down on your back, with knees up and feet grounded on the mat. If the low back is uncomfortable, place a firm bolster or cushion under the knees and let the legs release; feel the low back soften. A cushion under the neck is fine. (This can also be done sitting. Remember to sit as upright as possible).

Place hands gently on abdomen, thumbs at the navel. Let the elbows and shoulders sink into the mat.

Become aware of the body and the floor beneath supporting you. Give yourself a minute or two to just find ease and comfort.

Become aware of the breath, your natural breath. Let it be as it is, don't influence it in any way. Just let the breath flow. Let the exhalation travel out quietly to the end of its journey. Don't push, just let it go. Feel the body sinking into the floor with each exhalation.

Become aware of the movement of the breath in the body. Feel that you are breathing into your hands, resting softly at your abdomen. Be aware of the movement of the abdomen, rising gently with each inhalation, gently sinking with each exhalation.

When you breath in, know that you are breathing in. When you breath out, know that you are breathing out. Surrender the out breath. Let the in breath occur spontaneously. Trust the breath, just as you do when you are asleep.

Observe the breath and its movement in the abdomen for a minute or two.

Now move your hands up to the sides of the ribcage, so they are 'cradling' the ribs. Feel the movement of the rib cage as it lifts up and out with each inhalation, and as it sinks downwards and inwards with each exhalation. Continue this for a minute or two, observing the breath in the movement of the ribs and lower chest.

Then rest your hands gently on your upper chest, with your fingers pointing in and your thumbs just below your collarbones. Breathe into your hands and feel the movement of the top of the chest. Practice breathing into this area for about one minute. Release your hands to your sides.

Now let the breath flow into your abdomen, into your rib cage, and finally into your upper chest, in a continuous breath. Do not force or push the breath. Allow it to flow like waves on an ocean. Stay in this position for awhile just watching the breath and the wave of movement that travels from your abdomen to your rib cage to your chest as you inhale, and from your abdomen, to the rib cage, and finally the upper chest as you exhale. Let it flow of its own accord, no need for huge breaths , just seeing each part, abdomen, ribs, upper chest as three parts of the whole.
This three part breathing is called **full yogic breath, or diaphragmic breathing.**

A CALMING BREATH AND MOVEMENT EXERCISE

help worries melt away

Moving mindfully with the breath is another way to develop breath awareness. This can be extremely calming and centring, and particularly helpful when you are feeling 'all over the place'.

This exercise can be done standing or sitting.

Find your breath and allow it to flow naturally. Feel yourself connecting to the breath as you centre your attention on it.

On the inhalation, raise both arms forward until approximately hip level, no higher. As you exhale, allow them to come back down to the sides and to follow through behind to approximately hip level. Inhale, and repeat the arm action smoothly and slowly, to hip level in the front of the body on the inhalation and to hip level behind the body on the exhalation. Repeat four more times.

Next, inhale and raise the arms to waist level in front of the body on the inhalation, and let them flow behind the body to waist level on the exhalation. Repeat five more times. Let the breath and movement flow together with no rush or force, just thoughtful awareness.

Inhale and take your parallel arms forward to approximately shoulder height, and on the exhalation allow them to reach back behind the body to as high as is comfortably possible without arching the back. Repeat another five times.

Finally, just stand or sit quietly with the arms by your sides, observing the breath and how you feel now. How is the breath, has it lengthened? How is the body, has it released any tension, particularly in the shoulders? How is the mind, have your thoughts and emotions calmed down, even a little?

Notice that as the arm movements became slightly bigger in their arc of motion the breath, both the inhalation and the exhalation became slightly longer and more complete.

MEDITATION

quiet the mind

The mind connects us with both our external and internal environments, and is always busy giving us messages. That is its job. When we sit for meditation, hoping for peace and stillness, we become more aware of the mind's activities.

In our attempts and experiences at meditation our thoughts and emotions inevitably arise. We can become restless and impatient with the mind and with our inability to control it. The more we try to control and suppress it, the more insistently it clamours for our attention. And so we may ask ourselves, what am I supposed to be getting from meditation? What is meditation, if not a place to find inner peace and stillness?

One answer is that it is a practice of simply being with you, watching yourself, looking at what is there. The aim of meditation is to understand what we did not formerly understand, to see what we have not previously seen. This unfolding is different for each person. Meditation is, perhaps, discovery.

Meditation gives us the opportunity to look, in a detached sort of way, at the thoughts and emotions that unavoidably arise when we sit still, and this 'looking' process allows us to gain clarity on them. If we perceive our thoughts and emotions as simply distractions, and push them away impatiently, then this opportunity is lost. Everything that happens in our life, every reality needs to be seen and accepted as it is before there is possibility of change. We must know where we are in order to move forward. Meditation should not be an escape, or a retreat, but rather it should lead you into the light of reality.

We cannot make the mind a blank, we cannot make the mind be completely still, but we can slow it down. The mind, in its 'usual state' often has many tape loops that just won't stop. Or the mind may constantly roam from topic to topic, with running commentaries, or be busy having conversations over and over with someone, or flitting from worries, to our to-do lists, and so on. When all of these types of things are filling our mind, and then on top of all that, challenging emotions arrive to swamp us, how can we ever move towards an inner peace and eventual acceptance?

Many people do not even realise that they have a choice, that it is possible to slow and/or quiet this constant inner dialogue. Even when a person has experienced the benefits and sweet moments of inner calm, it is still very possible to feel almost up against a wall when it comes to sitting down to meditate. The onslaught of emotions that arise in times of difficulty can make the idea of sitting still and letting things come up be terrifying. Yet this therapeutic process will bring about integration and harmony on the physical, mental and emotional planes. Meditation is without a doubt a healing practice because repressing emotions traps energy and, over time, may lead to further illness or depression.

BENEFITS

- gaining conscious awareness of emotions, monitoring emotional patterns, finding ways to transform negative emotions, releasing challenging emotions

- better health; can lower blood pressure, slow heart rate, ease anxiety

- helps to manage pain

- sharpens your mind through developing the ability to focus and concentrate

- eases your suffering; heals body, mind, and spirit

- generates love and compassion

- helps to live mindfully, in the present moment

For thousands of years, many cultures have practised meditation because really there are many more benefits than the ones listed here. From the vast pool of knowledge from these cultures there are many different types of meditation practices. These different practices will suit different people, personalities and temperaments, at different stages of life. It is very worthwhile to explore different types, because what suits one person may not suit the next. You want to choose one that resonates with you.

Many meditations choose a single object to focus on; the breath, a sound, or an image. This focusing quiets the mind's chattering and allows emotions and thoughts to arise without judgement, so that we can let them go. The focusing gives your mind a simple repetitive task that will ultimately slow down the babbling and help the mind to be in a quieter state. When it is in this state, we can accept the clarity and detachment that we experience, as we let old thoughts and emotions arise and dissipate.

It is worth thinking about trying a technique for approximately 3-4 weeks, at least five minutes a day.

You may even want to keep a small journal logging down how you feel each day, before and after. You may find through your notes that you definitely feel drawn to one technique more than the others. This is the one that is right for you at this time. **Trust yourself.**

In general, meditation is done in a sitting position, whether it is on a chair or on a mat. However, all that is necessary is that the head, neck and spine are in a straight line. In times of illness, or recovery, when sitting for even five minutes seems impossible, you can choose to meditate, semi-reclined, or lying flat on your bed or mat.

The worst that will happen is that you will fall asleep!

Here is a list of how to settle into the body to prepare for a meditation practice:

- spine upright (or simply straight, if lying down) and lengthened

- back of the neck lengthened

- crown of the head releasing away from the body

- shoulders soft

- tongue resting gently in the mouth

- lips soft, cheeks soft

- eyelids gently closed

- forehead smooth, no frown

- hands soft, resting on the thighs, or in the lap

- body steady and still

Now you are ready to practice.

MEDITATION FOR
BEING ENOUGH JUST AS YOU ARE

acknowledge and accept that you are where you are in life, and it is enough

---

Begin by sitting in an upright position, or lying in a semi-reclined or fully reclined position. Place a cushion behind the back, or knees for support if needed. Rest your right hand on your thigh, palm facing upwards.

Take the left hand and place the palm in front of the centre of the chest (your heart centre) approximately 15 cm. (6 inches) from your heart.

As you say to yourself 'I am', move your left hand toward your chest, until it is only about 10 cm. (4 inches) from your heart.

On a second 'I am', take the hand about 30 cm (12 inches) from the chest. Inhale and draw the hand back to the original position.

Continue this cycle for five to ten minutes. With each movement of your hand you recognise to yourself that you are absolutely enough just as you are.
You are offering yourself compassion and acceptance as the hand draws near to the heart, and perhaps acknowledging to the Universe that you accept that you are where you are in life, and it is enough.

You are offering
yourself compassion
and acceptance as
the hand draws near
to the heart.

RELAXATION

bringing balance and connection to body, mind, emotions and spirit

---

Relaxation is a state in which there is no movement, no effort, and the brain is quiet. Scientists have researched the effects of relaxation and report measurable benefits, including reduction in muscle tension and improved circulation.

Relaxation is fundamental to our being. It is also a vital element in healing. It releases muscular and mental tension. It slows, regulates and calms breathing, and lowers the heart rate and blood pressure. As the body and mind let go, tension and anxiety give way to comfort, stillness and peace of mind. This quieter mental and emotional state is conducive to the repair of cells.

We need to understand that habits of tension develop over time, and that time is needed to overcome them. Relaxation is a practical skill, and like any other skill it needs to be learned. You may feel 'worse' at first as you grow more aware of your habitual tensions. This heightened awareness is the first step towards learning to relax, so regard it as progress.

Relaxation can restore a sense of inner harmony - resting for a period in a balanced state creates a resilient and stable mind - even in the face of stress. The deep rest that can occur during deep relaxation is different from sleep. Deep states of sleep include periods of dreaming, which may increase muscular tension and psychological signs of tension.

The moments of stillness that we experience in relaxation are not just pleasant interludes between periods of pressure and stress. The effects of relaxation are cumulative and lasting. Each time we go into a deeply relaxed state we learn something about letting go and this learning stays with us.

A yoga class almost always ends with a period of relaxation. It consolidates the benefits of all that has been done in the session, and gives a unique opportunity to experience being truly at rest. However, you can do a relaxation at any time. If feeling tired, listless, or feeling the need for a lift try turning to relaxation for relief. There are many wonderful CDs of guided relaxations and an unimaginable number are available on YouTube too. Pick a voice that resonates with you, and begin to explore this wonderful method of self-care.

Relaxation is a practical skill, and like any other skill it needs to be learned.

MUSCLE RELEASE RELAXATION

twenty minutes of profound relaxation is equivalent to five hours sleep

It is said that twenty minutes of profound relaxation is equivalent to five hours sleep so it is an invaluable means to learn to be able to help one's self. It may sound like a simple thing, to lie down and do nothing; however it can be one of the most difficult things to master. It is also one of the most important. This method is simple and can be done on your own.

Lie down and get comfortable, using cushions under head, knees and even heels to find the support you need to be able to be in a place where you can rest for awhile without moving. Cover yourself with a blanket. Some people like to have their hands resting on their abdomen; others prefer their arms slightly away from their sides, usually with the palms facing up. Have the legs a little apart whichever way feels comfortable to you.

Close your eyes and connect to your breath. Just spend a minute or two watching your breathing; feeling and observing your breath as it moves through the body of its own accord. Let it be, trust it as you do when you are asleep.

Now go through each body part, first tensing it and then releasing it. Start with your feet and work your way up through your legs; calves and shins front and back of the thighs; and the hips. Move to your hands, arms, and shoulders. Tense and release the buttocks, the, back, abdomen, chest, and throat. Move on to the face, the jaws, the lips, the eyes, cheeks, forehead, and scalp. At each body part, really send your awareness into it and feel the tensing and releasing. Enjoy it. Try not to let your mind wander, but if it does, just gently guide it back.

As you work your way though the body, you should feel a deep sense of release and relaxation seeping into the body. Feel yourself sinking into the support beneath you. Let all tension flow away. When you have completed the whole body, just be aware of the entire body resting. Be here a while and just observe the breath flowing in and out, letting everything just be still and at rest. Notice the peace and stillness within you and around you. Tell yourself you can hold on to this tranquil calmness and carry it with you throughout your day.

When you are ready to re-enter your day, do so slowly and mindfully. Wriggle the limbs gently, roll on to your side. Be here a moment or two and you open your eyes. Sit up slowly and pause there for a few breaths before continuing to get up. This technique can be practised sitting supported in a chair as well.

At each body part, really send your awareness into it and feel the tensing and releasing.

16 POINT RELAXATION PRACTICE

This short and effective practice is easy to learn. With inhalation we bring our awareness to each of the 16 parts of the body, with exhalation, we just think of letting go. It takes approximately five minutes, and can bring about a surprisingly full relaxation response. It can be practiced independently of a teacher, and has the benefit of being easy to remember.

You don't have to concentrate. Simply move your awareness lightly from each part of the body to the next. Get into a comfortable relaxation posture. This can be lying flat, or with a bolster under the knees, lying on your side, or even on your tummy. It can also be practiced sitting in a chair. It can be practiced in bed to encourage sleep.

With each out breath, feel the body part melting into the support beneath it.
Allow the breath to flow naturally and easily.

On each inhalation you bring your awareness to the body part, for example:

Breathing in, bring your awareness to your feet.

Breathing out, let go.

Continue on with each part as follows:

Feet, shins, kneecaps, thighs, abdomen, solar plexus, chest, spine,

Hands, forearms, upper arms, throat, back of the head, jaw, eyes, scalp.

At first, keep to one breath for each part of the body. Then, if you have the time for a longer practice, you can let your attention rest at each point for 2-3 breaths.

Take your time coming out of any
relaxation, slowly beginning to move
the body; wriggling fingers and toes,
rocking limbs gently, opening eyes
and allowing gaze to softly return, and
taking your time coming out of your
relaxation posture. You don't want to
shock the nervous system after just
having given it a chance to calm down.

MOVEMENT

no matter how sick a person may be, within them is a healthy being

Our body is made for movement. People living with physical limitations from living with cancer or life changing illness may be fearful of starting an activity. However, with thought and care, gentle movement is not only beneficial but positively empowering.

Think of it this way. No matter how sick a person may be, within them is a healthy being. Yoga movement is one of the tools that will allow us to awaken and support that vital part of ourselves.

The wonderful thing about yoga movement is that it is non-competitive so you really can work at your own pace. The movements do not have to be big to be powerful. A person does not have to become a human pretzel. Gentle mindful movements, with full awareness, and synchronized with the breath can address tension and blockages of energy.

Doing yoga movement and postures will help your whole system and move you towards better health and energy levels. Your breathing will improve. Your circulation, digestive, endocrine and nervous systems; your organs, muscles, and your bones will all benefit. Range of motion, flexibility, and strength are all enhanced by yoga postures. Your mind will gain stability, your ability to focus and concentrate will improve.

Even when one's energy level is extremely low, one can find ease from the most gentle of movements a few minutes a day. Posture work can be infinitely tailored to accommodate a healing body. Gentle rotation of joints is enough movement to get the energy and circulation flowing, to move the muscles directly around the joints and to break up tense holding patterns.

Yoga postures require us to become aware of our bodies -they break down the distance from ourselves and bring us into contact with our own sensations and feelings. This may allow us to change our attitude that can help to change our relationship to our illness and to our healing.

In times of illness it is important to find simple practices that do not make strenuous demands and that can nurture and restore. It is a time to learn how to listen to your body and accept that what you can do is truly enough. Learn to trust your body and your intuition. Let yourself enjoy how yoga movement can bring your body, mind and spirit into harmony.

GENTLE CHAIR PRACTICE

some gentle movements which can be carried out whilst sitting

Sit as tall as possible on a firm chair. Use a cushion behind the back for support if you like. Have your feet on the floor, under your knees, hip distance apart. Let all of the movements be done with the breath, keeping it slow, steady and gentle.

After doing the ten postures, just sit quietly for a couple of minutes and observe how your body and mind feel, and how your breath is now having done a practice. Remember you can pause and rest and listen to your body at any time, or do only some of them.

It is important that you get your medical professional's permission before doing any exercise. They will help you to know if it is a good time for you to begin a practice of mindful movement.

After doing the
nine postures,
just sit quietly and
observe how your
body and mind feel.

1

Shoulder Circles

Bring the shoulders forward, then up to your ears, then back and down. The arms are at the side of body, hands may rest in lap. Repeat three times in each direction.

2

Neck Releases

Inhale, and exhale turn chin over right shoulder, keeping it level with the floor. Exhale brings your chin back to centre. Inhale, take chin over left shoulder. Exhale the chin back to centre. Repeat three times to each side.

3

Arm Raises

Inhale, turn the palms up and lift the outstretched arms out away from body and as high as is comfortable for you. Exhale, turn the palms to face down, and let the outstretched arms return to the sides of the body. Repeat three to six times, moving with the breath.

Arm Opening

Begin with hands pressed lightly together at the heart. Inhale and open the arms out to the sides, taking them as far back as is comfortable. Exhale; return the hands to in front of the heart. Keep the arms near to shoulder height throughout if possible. Feel the chest stretch open when arms go out.

4

5

Spinal Curls

Sit tall in the chair. Inhale and on exhale, drop chin towards chest and slowly roll the shoulders forward and let the spine curl forward and down, going only as far as is comfortable for you. Your hands may slide down your legs, or holding legs of chair for support. This is a gentle forward bending movement. Slowly curl the spine up again. Repeat three times. Sit to the front of chair so the arms are in line with the legs of the chair. Inhale and sit up. Exhale and let the right hand slide down the right leg of chair. Feel the spine bending sideways like a bamboo in the wind. The left arm is passive at the left side of the body. Slowly inhale and raise body back to centre. Repeat on other side. Do both sides three times.

6

Cat Pose

Place hands on knees. Inhale and lift chest, hollowing back and lifting the entire spine up. Look up as much as comfortable. Exhale, and draw in the abdomen, rounding the back and spine and softly release the head forward. Repeat three times moving with the breath.

7

Hip Circles

Sit to the front of chair. The left hand can hold the chair. The right hand holds the outer right thigh. Draw circles slowly and mindfully with the right knee allowing the right leg to circle as big as is comfortable for you. Do three circles each direction and then switch and do the same the left side.

8

Leg Raises

Sit at the front of the chair. Let both hands gently clasp the back of right thigh. Inhale and lift the lower leg, straightening the leg. Exhale, softly lower the lower leg and foot back to starting position. Do three to six on the right side and then repeat on the left side.

Star Pose

Sit towards the front of the chair. Stretch the legs wide apart, letting the legs straighten and the heels stay on the floor. Inhale and stretch the arms out too, adopting a star position, stretching throughout the whole body. Exhale and let the arms rest down in lap and the legs return to the centre. Repeat three times, stretching each time only as far as comfortable for you.

9

BEING OUTSIDE AND WALKING

a wonderful low impact form of exercise that also lifts the mood

---

Being outside is a positive thing that you can do for yourself. Even sitting out is beneficial. We take in energy from the food that we eat, the air that we breathe and from sunlight. Being outside boosts Vitamin D levels and it enhances mood.

Walking outside is a wonderful low impact form of exercise. It lubricates stiff joints and eases away muscle tension as the arms swing and the legs move. It stimulates and strengthens the heart and bones. The 'feel good' endorphins released reduce stress and anxiety. Researchers in America and the United Kingdom both agree that it can relieve mild depression.

One can begin by walking back and forth in the garden, or to the end of the block and back. Use a cane or walking stick for support if needed, or the arm of a companion. There is no set speed that one must achieve to feel the benefits of walking, so listen to your body and let it determine where you start, how far you go and how you progress. It may not be long at all before what was a five minute exercise becomes a twenty minute one. And you may be surprised at how it can become an integral part of your day, a routine that is sorely missed by body and mind when passed by.

The 'feel good'
endorphins released
reduce stress
and anxiety.

ACKNOWLEDGEMENTS

Thanks to Elm House Creative Advertising and Design Agency, Belfast for their invaluable advice and creative input in the design of this project.

Particular thanks to Chris Heaney for the mouth-watering photographs that bring these recipes to life and to Claire Rankin for her assistance in food styling.

With special thanks to Roche Products for providing a grant towards the production of this book.